The Evacuee Girl

To Megan
with best wishes
Jean Reddy

The Evacuee Girl

Jean Reddy

First published in 2005 by
Stamford House Publishing

ISBN: 1-904985-40-8

Printed and bound in Great Britain by:
Stamford House Publishing
7 The Metro Centre
Woodston
Peterborough
PE2 7UH

DEDICATION

I dedicate this book to my brother Ron,
who was infinitely precious to me,
and who encouraged me to meet the challenges of life.

I miss you.

Contents

THE EVACUEE GIRL

Chapter 1

September 1947

Margaret Trent didn't realise she was just seven years of age when she made the unconscious decision as to what she wanted to be when she grew up. Her ambition, she knew, was to care for children. She could not understand why but perhaps her own sad experiences had fostered the germ of ambition.

As she sat gazing over the rippling water of the River Thames, on that beautiful calm sunny day, her thoughts drifted back over the past seven years. She was aware her life had changed dramatically because of her own unfortunate experiences and feelings of loneliness and unhappiness. Surely there must be others equally as unhappy as her, and she felt positive that she would never be the same person who had naively embarked on that fateful journey to Wales in September 1942.

So many children had been evacuated from the City of London and its suburbs. Packed up and shipped off like parcels, with labels round their necks and no idea when they would be able to go home again.

Just three months before she herself had been evacuated she had been living at home in Upminster in Essex with her widowed mother and youngest brother, John

If only time could have stood still.

*

Margaret had been the youngest child of the family. Although a good girl, she was also a mischievous six-year-old. Her pale blue eyes and her small turned up nose gave her an elf-like appearance; and her short cut blonde hair made her seem angelic.

Her mother's Victorian attitude, that children should be seen and not heard, had an enormous influence on her and contributed to the fact that she was rather a shy child.

Her elder sister May was married and living in London with her husband and small child Terry. May had married against her mother's wishes, and their mother blamed the marriage for causing her husband's illness, so Margaret rarely saw her sister.

William, her eldest brother, was serving in the Royal Air Force, and she only saw him occasionally when he came home on leave, wearing his blue uniform. His leave was never more than a couple of days, so she hardly knew him. She liked William, he was always so cheerful and full of life, and would sweep her up into his arms when he came, and then tickle her to death at times, causing her to screech with giggles and laughter.

Then there was Robbie, just two years younger than William, who was away at sea in the Royal Navy. Robbie had blonde hair like her, and was very slim, whereas William was rather stocky. Her mother always told her that her two oldest brothers were away "at war".

Which left John, her thirteen-year-old brother, who was studying at college. She was very fond of him, and often helped him with his early morning paper round, and on Sundays John would take her with him to St Lawrence's Church, where he was a server. Margaret would dutifully give out hymn books to the congregation as they arrived, which to her was a very important job, before taking her seat for the service. Going to Church was for her the highlight of her week, she loved it; a friendly place where the vicar always stopped and talked to her, and patted her on the head saying, "Bless you my child".

She followed her young brother around whenever she could. He on the other hand tolerated his younger sister's undying devotion. John and she had a lot in common. He played the piano and was having lessons. Margaret tried to copy the tunes she heard him play. She would sit at the family piano and pretend she was playing beautiful music. They both loved classical music, and both loved listening to the wireless together. They liked nothing better than hearing their favourite pianist playing Chopin's melodic waltzes and nocturnes, or Dame Myra Hess playing "Jesu' Joy of Man's Desiring". They would lose themselves in the haunting tunes. Margaret would often drift away on a voyage of imagination. How she loved the quiet evenings, which were so peaceful, but more often than not those evenings were interrupted by the sounds of sirens, warning people to evacuate their homes, and make for the nearest air-raid shelter.

Their mother always drew the blackout curtains each evening, but on one such evening she forgot, and the ARP Warden knocked at the door, and told her in no uncertain terms to draw them.

Some months before, William, Robbie and John had been busy digging a very big hole in the garden; it had certainly spoilt one of the large rose bush beds, which had totally disappeared. Lots of corrugated iron was delivered, which was gradually erected into an Anderson Shelter of their own. Margaret had initially thought this great fun; a little house, sunk into the ground in the garden. Lots of earth was placed on top of it, and she derived much pleasure from running up on top of the shelter singing "I'm the King of the Castle, get down you dirty rascal".

When the shelter was nearly finished, she was allowed to go down the steep steps and look around inside. The boys had erected five bunk beds, all covered in sacking. There was a small table which she knew had come from inside the house, and a low chair. On the table was a Tilley lamp. John told her that the small bed at the end was hers. She ran over and climbed onto it. It seemed fun, but she didn't like the dark, it was very spooky.

One night when the sirens had sounded, John and her mother took her down into the dugout. John had lit the lamp, and her mother sat clicking away with her knitting needles. She was forever knitting socks for the boys. Margaret lay down on her bunk and was just drifting off to sleep, when all of a sudden she felt something crawl across her face. She screamed, causing her mother to drop her knitting.

'Whatever is the matter,' her mother cried.

'Something walked over my face.' Margaret jumped down to the floor.

John just laughed, 'It was probably just a spider,' he said.

Both John and Margaret tried hard not to take in what was happening around them, though they knew that the enemy planes were dropping bombs, and they had come to know the sounds of doodlebugs flying over, and became frightened if the engine noise stopped, as this meant that the instrument of death would fall from the sky, creating havoc. Sometimes after one had crashed they would spend time hunting for the shrapnel; pieces of jagged metal, which could be found lying about the roads. People viewed these as trophies, and Margaret longed to own one.

On quiet evenings they also pitted their wits over jigsaw puzzles, the larger the better, as well as reading books. John used to read two comics called the "Hotspur" and the "Beano". She enjoyed him telling her about the adventures of Desperate Dan. Yes, they were most compatible, and cared about each other's well being.

Their father had died from a stroke earlier that year. It had been a terribly upsetting time. Their mother was left to bring up her two youngest children as best she could. There was no welfare state at the time, and she had to go out to work each day. Margaret, being only six years of age when this happened, was unable to understand what dying meant. She did understand that her father was not around any more, nor sitting in his favourite chair; but she accepted the fact when her mother told her that he was somewhere else, waiting for them.

She had loved her father. Although he had been seriously ill for some time, he had idolised his daughter, and tended to spoil her. She missed climbing on his lap, which she always found was a safe haven, especially when her mother's strict rules and practices came to haunt her. Her father always took her side, and she adored him.

Not long after her father had died, John told his sister why he had been away from home until recently. True, when John had not been around, there had been no fun, and no one to confide in, these last few months had been wonderful. Her mother had always been busy looking after their father, and had given very little time to her. She had been lonely, but now John was back at home all was well again with her little world.

John told her about the "war", as much as he knew, and said he had been evacuated to a family in Maidenhead, for his own safety; or so mother had said. He told her he had lived with two families. He was not sure why it had been safe for his mother and baby sister to be at home, when it was unsafe for him.

However, he told Margaret that he had quite liked the first family he had lived with and that he missed them quite a lot now. He never told her about how he had been treated by other children in the area where he had stayed, who looked down on the "vacci's", and excluded him from playing with them. Something had prompted him not to say this.

Firstly, he had been placed with an elderly couple who had two deaf mute children. He explained that this was where he had learned the deaf and dumb language. John showed Margaret how he could talk with his hands by making signs. He had thoroughly enjoyed it there, but when their mother had visited him, she had been shocked to learn that he hadn't had a bath, so he was moved very quickly.

He had been transferred to another family where he had remained for the remainder of his stay. Mother approved of the second family, and he had fond memories of his time away from home.

*

Margaret's family lived in a very comfortable, three-bedroomed, semi-detached house in a quiet avenue, which in those days was rented from a landlord. She knew the landlord quite well as he lived in the same road, and often Margaret or John took the rent card to him, with the money their mother gave them.

Their rented house had a beautiful garden, full of rose bushes. Beyond the lawn you went through an archway covered in climbing roses, to where the vegetables were grown, and lots of chickens roamed in a large pen, as well as two ducks who had a pen of their own.

Her bedroom, which was the smallest, overlooked the Avenue, and often she would sit in the window seat and look out, watching what other people were doing. There was the man across the road, who always tended his garden every day, and mowed his front lawn quite often. He appeared to be a nice man, who chatted to lots of people as they passed by. Then there was the lady who lived next door, who would go out on her bicycle to do some shopping, coming back with the basket resting on the front of her bike, full of packages.

Margaret could see children playing hopscotch on the pavement a little further down the road. How she would love to join them, but her mother didn't approve of her mixing with other children.

It was more fun watching when it was raining, and she felt safe, warm and dry up in her bedroom. There would be people under umbrellas, hurrying along to get out of the rain. She could see them, all wet, and sometimes straggly. Yes, this was a time she liked her house.

Being the youngest child in the family, her ambition then had been to grow up as quickly as she could. She often felt left out of things, and had to go to bed early. She desperately wanted to be grown up like her brothers and sister, and gain her mother's attention and respect. She was conscious that her mother doted on the oldest three, and had very little time for herself.

When William came home on leave, her mother would run around making him tea, and cooking special meals for him. He was treated like the Prodigal Son.

She later learnt that he would bring home packets of tea and butter, and things that were hard to come by, such as bacon and meat. She had no idea where he got them from.

Her mother's larder was often empty, and she was told this was due to the war. There was rationing on, and people were only allowed so much of each item. Rationing had been in force since January 1940, some two years. When John was home, she used to swap some items with him.

Each person was allowed 2 oz of butter, and 4 oz of sugar each week. John could not bear to drink his tea without sugar, and Margaret hated eating bread without butter, so they would each swap their ration. Bacon too was in short supply and a luxury, but often mother would find a rasher or two for William's tea when he was home.

They were very lucky that they had the chickens, but even so her mother had to give so many of the eggs laid to the government stores.

Her mother also stored tinned dried egg and milk powder for emergencies, William used to bring these home in his kit bag. John used to say he got it on the black market. Margaret could not envisage what this meant at all.

*

One day, at the end of the summer of 1942, everything in Margaret's world changed and came to an abrupt end.

On going upstairs she found her mother packing an old tatty suitcase with some of the clothes from her chest of drawers, which was in her small bedroom.

Her mother turned round when she heard Margaret approach; she sat the child down on the bed and said, 'Ah, there you are. I was about to come and tell you that you are going on a journey to Wales. You will only be allowed to take a few things with you; but it shouldn't be for long.'

Margaret became excited, and assumed that her mother and brother were going as well. She was quickly to be disillusioned. Her mother told her she would be going on her own, along with a lot of other children from the area, and she would know some of them from the local school.

She immediately began to panic. 'Where is Wales, Mummy?' she asked.

Her mother replied, 'It is quite a long way, and you will go on a coach and a train to get there, but it won't be for very long, as the war should be over soon, then you can come home.'

She was unaware that she was being evacuated, nor that she was unlikely to return for some three years.

* * *

Chapter 2

There were only two days before she would board the coach that was to take her to London, to join the train going north. Not really a lot of time to say goodbye to her friends. She could only take a change of clothing and her gas mask. She hated to leave her favourite doll behind, but she just had to take her teddy. She always took Mr Growler to bed with her each night. And then there was the family dog, Bobbie. Oh goodness, she would hate not seeing him each day. She was so confused.

Why did she have to go? Everything was explained as "the war". Her brother John reassured her it would be all right. 'You remember my telling you about my going for two years, don't you?' he asked her.

'Yes, but Mummy said the war is nearly over, and it will only be for a little while.'

'Well, there you are then,' he replied, 'and you will be safe from those doodlebugs which keep coming over.'

'But we all go down into the air raid shelter in the garden when they come over,' she pleaded with him. She hated going down there, although there were little camp beds, it was dark, even with the gas lamp, and she hated the spiders which sometimes crawled over her. But it was better than going a long way away.

Her mother also tried to reassure her, but it was all to no avail, and soon the few items she could take, her silver hairbrush and mirror, toothbrush and paste, her slippers, and a photograph of her mother were all packed into the old small suitcase, along with the clothes that she would take with her.

*

The dreaded day dawned. It was miserable and cold, but the rain held off. This was as well, as she had on her best dress and shoes, and she didn't want to get them wet and messy. She carried her coat, gas mask and suitcase. Her mother made her promise she would take care of her suitcase, and be a good girl. Goodness, Mummy was crying; but Margaret felt excited, as well as having a curious feeling of confusion.

At the school, where she was to board the coach, she saw some of her school friends. This made her feel better. She would know some people, and in a few days they would come back, she thought. After all, it could only be for a few days, she had hardly any spare clothing with her, and most of her clothes were still at home. Mummy was just being silly. Anyway, she could look after herself.

Margaret climbed up into the coach, and sat next to a girl she knew called Jenny. Jenny had long dark hair tied up in a pony tail. She was sitting next to the window and waving frantically to her mother, who was standing next to her own mother. There was a lot of noise, and other children pushed down the coach, all trying to get into the back seat.

The goodbyes were said, and the coach eventually pulled out for London. What an adventure! She had never been anywhere without her mother before. It was quite a pleasant journey and there was a lot of chatter going on between the children. Margaret clutched the little brown paper bag containing some jam sandwiches. Her mother had told her to keep them until she was on the train.

'You have a long way to go,' she had said, 'keep your sandwiches to eat on the train.' Margaret was tempted to eat one, but decided not to.

Jenny didn't talk much at first. She stared out of the window, and looked rather apprehensive.

They drove past lots of fields, and through small towns, before gradually coming into the big City of London. There were so many big buildings, and lots of houses, and blocks of flats. Margaret had never seen anything like it. Some of the buildings had been bombed and piles of rubble lay on the pavements and in the road. The traffic became very busy and the coach crawled along the roads, stopping continually at traffic lights.

Jenny suddenly asked, 'Where are we going?'

'I don't know for sure,' Margaret replied, 'my mother said we are going to North Wales.'

'We have come a long way,' Jenny continued, 'do you think we are nearly there?'

'I don't think so Jenny, we have to go on a train yet,' she told the girl.

At last they were at the big station – Euston Station in London. The coach pulled into a lay-by at the side of the station. As they alighted from the coach, Margaret looked around. There was so much noise, and goodness, lots of big steam trains. The loudspeaker was booming out some information, which nobody seemed to be listening to.

There were soldiers in khaki uniforms walking about with kit bags over their shoulders. Young men in Air Force blue uniforms, just like her brother William's, all animatedly chatting to people. Sailors stood around in groups. Women were crying and obviously saying goodbye to loved ones. Porters were hurrying along with suitcases, and lots of people were shouting. So many people, and so many trains. Margaret was fascinated, but also very frightened, confused and bewildered.

She moved nearer to her group. All the children were assembled ready for the journey, but they were all ill prepared for the length of it. Labelled like luggage, they were to set off into the unknown, their lives changed forever, by a war many knew little about.

Each child's label stated their name and home address; the people escorting the children tied the labels to the children's coat buttons, or onto their gas masks. The children were placed in different groups and moved in crocodile fashion towards one of the big steam trains.

Margaret boarded the train, as instructed, but realised that her school friend Jenny, who she had been sitting with on the coach, was not in her group. She started to feel lonely and scared, and started to cry. One of the ladies looking after the children came and ushered Margaret to a seat on the train, and sat next to her.

She told Margaret that her name was Miss Hindley. She put her arms around the child and said, 'Don't worry dear, we are all going together, and when we get to North Wales, you will enjoy it.' She went on, 'I will be nearby all the time while we are on the train, and if you are worried about anything, just come and see me.' Margaret nodded, and Miss Hindley moved along the train, talking to each child in turn.

After a while Margaret began to feel a little better, and was told she could eat her sandwiches when she wanted to. She looked down at the little brown paper bag, and remembered seeing her mother preparing them for her earlier that morning. This brought a smile to her face. Her mother had expected her to be a big girl, so that was what she must be.

Margaret continued to eat her sandwiches, which by now were rather dry, but she was hungry and soon devoured them all. She found great enjoyment playing a game of "I Spy" with some of the other children in the carriage. Unfortunately, some of them couldn't spell very well, so they were often looking round for things starting with the wrong letters, and they made an argument about this.

Some hours later, the ladies in charge of the children told them to start getting their things together as they were approaching Crewe, and would have to change trains. They were to be sure they left nothing behind on the train. As the train pulled into the station, Margaret saw the big boards on the platform with big letters on them, which said CREWE.

All the children were shepherded off the train, and had to stand around for what seemed ages. Margaret became tired and sat on her old sturdy, but shabby, suitcase. It was very old fashioned, and very scratched, but it sustained her weight, as she was very slim and lithe.

Crewe was another very busy station, but not as grand as Euston. People kept jostling each other, and everything appeared hectic. Margaret kept close to her group and Miss Hindley. They had to change platforms, which entailed them walking sedately in line over to Platform 3, where another train was waiting to take them further on their journey.

Her mother hadn't told her about this, and she wondered if her mother really knew where she was going.

The children were all eager to climb onto the train and get comfortable once more. It was not long before the train started off again, but they only went as far as Chester, and once again they had to change trains, this time on to one going directly to Wrexham.

Their journey had taken most of the day, and finally they arrived at their destination – Wrexham.

*

Margaret didn't know where she was. *This must be Wales,* she thought. She was by now feeling rather homesick and wished her mother were meeting her from the train. Miss Hindley came along and ushered Margaret onto the platform.

'There my dear,' she said, 'not far to go now, we are all going in that coach you can just see at the other side of the barrier, and in half an hour we will be at the Memorial Church Hall, where we will all have some nice orange squash and biscuits.

The sandwiches had long since gone, and most of the children were hungry, as well as very tired.

The children were once again re-grouped as they emerged and moved along the platform, and once more they were taken in crocodile fashion, all struggling with their belongings, to the outside of the station, where they boarded the coach.

It was drizzling with rain, and most of the happy chatter had ceased. It was only a short journey to the Memorial Church Hall. Watching out of the window, Margaret saw lots of houses, with some fields in the background.

There was a park on one side of the road, and she could just make out some swings, a slide, and a roundabout, in one corner. On the other side of the road was a big gasometer, just a little way ahead. Everything looked damp and miserable, and her spirits were very low.

The coach stopped outside a dark looking building, where the two big doors stood open at the front. There were many people inside, who she could see standing around talking. The children once more collected all their things together and were led into the big hall, which had a stage at one end. Once inside, she could see all the people, and many children. *What were they all doing there?* she wondered.

The children from London queued up for a drink and some biscuits, which were soon demolished, and much appreciated. Then they all lined up and were told to gradually move up onto the stage, in turn.

Six children at a time moved onto the stage. There were some two dozen on it when Margaret joined them.

Gradually the children had their names called. People from the hall were pointing at certain children. As their names were called they were handed over to various families who were offering to care for them.

She continued to stand there in her best pink linen dress, which had little navy and white ducks printed on it and a crisp white collar. She knew she was tired but she still looked well dressed, but no one was choosing her.

* * *

Chapter 3

At last her name was called, and she was introduced to Mr and Mrs Jones, and their six children. Mr Jones took her small suitcase and everyone followed him outside. There they all stood round in a group and looked at her. Mrs Jones introduced herself, and then all the children.

Jim was the eldest, he was fourteen. He was slim and lanky, with a spotty face. His hair was stuck up and looked uncombed, and in his hands he was carrying a grey cap. Then there was Jane who was twelve. She had pretty auburn hair tied up in a pony tail, but it was very curly. She had lovely green eyes and smiled warmly at Margaret.

'Hello,' she said, 'I'm Jane, and you will be sleeping in my bedroom.'

Then there were the twins, Timmy and Peter, who were ten years of age, who sniggered together all the time, and obviously were sharing a private joke. Their father kept telling them to stand still and say hello.

Margaret turned her attention to the two youngest children Toby, and Elizabeth. Toby looked friendly, and said 'Hello, I am five,' very importantly, and went on 'I have a tricycle and you can ride it if you want to.' Margaret smiled and thanked him.

Which left Elizabeth who was seven years; the same age as herself. She thought, *Someone I can play with;* but Elizabeth soon made it quite obvious that their guest was beneath her. 'I have my own bedroom, and you are not to go in and touch my things,' she said.

Mrs Jones turned round on hearing this and remonstrated with the child. 'Elizabeth, that isn't very nice.'

Margaret didn't know what to make of it all. Such a large family. She thought of how different her own family had been at home. They all spoke funny as well, and it was hard for her to understand them sometimes.

*

All the little groups were starting to move off down the road. Margaret saw some of the children she had been with on the train, walking along with other people.

They walked a long way along many roads until they came to the house where the Jones family lived. 31 Salisbury Road. It was not a very impressive house. It was terraced, and the front door opened directly into the sitting room. Outside there was no front garden, you stepped directly onto the pavement. The roof was made of grey slate.

Inside however, it was fairly large, but it had no nice garden at the back like at home, just a back yard. Margaret discovered this when she asked to go to the toilet, and learned that it was outside in the yard.

Mrs Jones then told her to go with Jane upstairs, and she would show her where she was going to sleep. *What a strange house,* she thought. From the sitting room you went through a door into the kitchen-cum-dining room, then through into a small scullery. On the left wall there appeared to be a cupboard, but she was surprised that when the door was opened, there was a set of stairs going up.

'Come on Margaret,' said Jane, 'bring your suitcase up and I'll help you put your things away.' They climbed up the steep stairs. Margaret found it difficult to lift the case up the stairs but eventually she made it.

There were five bedrooms. The smallest belonged to Elizabeth, she was told. The twins had the next smallest, and had bunk beds. Mr & Mrs Jones had the largest room, and had a big double bed taking up most of the space, with so much furniture and clutter it looked very cramped. The quilt on their bed looked to be made up of lots of pieces of scrap material. The next room belonged to Jim and Toby.

Jane took Margaret into a room at the back of the house, which overlooked the back yard. It had one ordinary single bed in it and a small camp bed over in the corner. She learnt that this was for her. Jane moved toward the chest of drawers and said, 'You can have two drawers to put your things in.' She smiled at Margaret and said 'There is another toilet at the end of the landing.' and went on to say, 'we have a bath once a week. Dad gets the tin bath in from the yard, and puts it in front of the boiler in the kitchen, then he fills it with hot water from the copper, then we take it in turns to get in.' Margaret was horrified. *Bath in the kitchen! Would anyone else be there?* Oh no, she was used to having a bath in a proper bathroom at home.

She was still feeling quite stunned by this information when Jane said, 'Come on, let's go down and help lay the table for tea.' She went on, 'We all have jobs to do, and I lay the table.' She turned to Margaret and said, 'You can help me, tea is late today with your coming.' So she followed Jane downstairs.

Mrs Jones was in the kitchen preparing some food. Mr Jones was complaining about the next-door neighbour to his wife. Margaret helped set the table, but when everyone was called to have tea she soon learned that she would not be sitting at the table with everyone else. Her plate had been set out on the enamel worktop of the mangle in the scullery. She was told by Mrs Jones that there was not enough room for her at the table. She ate her tea, but she didn't feel very hungry sitting all on her own in the scullery. She suddenly felt so very unhappy and wanted to run away and cry.

Even though she was distraught, she had no one to turn to. She couldn't go and see Bobbie her dog, or her dear brother John, they were far away. Here she was in a strange house, with strange people, who had seemed quite nice at the Memorial Hall, but now didn't want her to sit with them for tea.

After everyone had finished she was expected to clear away the dishes from the table, and Jane washed up. Timmy dried up, but he was told off on more than one occasion to do it properly. How he didn't break anything was a miracle.

Margaret was very tired, and at 7 o'clock was allowed to go up to bed. 'I don't go to bed until half past seven,' pointed out Elizabeth. Margaret didn't care about this piece of boasting. She climbed the stairs, changed into her nightdress, put Mr Growler into her bed next to her, and the next minute she was fast asleep. She was too tired to notice how uncomfortable the little camp bed was.

*

She woke the following morning to a lot of noise. Everyone was dashing about, getting dressed quickly. She got up, wanting to use the toilet but couldn't get into the one upstairs, so she went down the stairs, and out into the back yard. She really couldn't stop shivering, and was glad when she went back upstairs to put on the clothes she had taken off the night before. Her lovely best dress was all crumpled. Her mother would have been cross.

Jane told her they all had to wash in the scullery. She followed her downstairs. There was a big brass tap over the large brown earthenware sink. She couldn't reach the tap. Jane turned it on for her. Ooh, the water was freezing cold. She wiped her face and hands and went to sit by the mangle.

She had sat there some while when Mrs Jones came up to her and said, 'It is no good sitting there Margaret, you have to help yourself.' She went on 'There is porridge in the saucepan on the stove, or there is some bread and dripping.'

She didn't fancy either. However, she was hungry, and decided to have a little porridge. Ugh! It tasted awful. How she missed her mother giving her a fresh boiled egg from their chickens at the bottom of the garden. Fresh eggs were always available at home.

The children of the family all donned their coats and picked up bags and satchels and left for school. Margaret went to go upstairs to get her coat and brush her hair. Mrs Jones saw her and said, 'You will be staying with me. You can dry the dishes and put them away in the cupboard, over there.

'But I go to school at home,' Margaret said to her.

'Well, you may have done, but here you will have to earn your keep.'

Margaret did as she was bid, she dried up as best she could, and while she was putting the plates away Mrs Jones said, 'You can clean and polish the brass fender, and then help me make the beds.'

During the course of the day, Margaret was expected to help Mrs Jones with the clothes to be laundered. Firstly bringing the dirty clothes downstairs from the bedrooms, and after they had been soaked and washed in the scullery sink, she had to turn the handle of the mangle, while Mrs Jones put them through the rollers, to squeeze the water out. They only stopped at 1 o'clock to have some of the dreadful bread and dripping that Mrs Jones seemed to like.

Margaret was devastated. Her own mother never expected her to do all these things, and although she had some chores to do at home they seemed easy compared with what she had done all morning, and there was still the afternoon to go yet. The washing was all hanging on the line in the yard, not getting any drier. There was no fire to keep warm by and she was very cold in her best dress, so she sneaked upstairs to cuddle Mr Growler. However, Mrs Jones soon missed her and called her down, giving her more work to do.

In what seemed no time at all the children started returning home from school. Jane brought in young Toby, it was her job to collect him from the infants' school. Elizabeth came in with the twins, and some little while later Jim arrived. He had stayed late at school to play football. He was all muddy, and was soon sent off to the scullery to wash himself.

The tea table was laid, and Mrs Jones cooked a meagre meal, a sort of stew. It was put on the table just as Mr Jones came in from work. He was a labourer at the local slate quarry. He was very dirty and went straight to the scullery to have a wash. He then sat down at the table in his dirty clothes, and doled out a scoop of stew to everyone from a large tureen. Margaret took hers to the mangle table and ate it. It was very hot, but tasteless. Not like the food her mother made. Jane cleared the big table and washed up. It was Peter's turn to dry the dishes.

Mrs Jones called Margaret into the scullery a little while later and said, 'After dinner each evening you can clean all the children's shoes ready for them to go to school.' She pointed to a cupboard where the polish and dusters were kept. There were small and large brushes, and tins of black and brown polish.

Six pairs of shoes! Margaret was mortified. She had never cleaned shoes before. She got the polish all over her hands and some on her best dress, Oh goodness, her mother would be cross when she saw it. She was really tired and wanting to go to bed. Margaret had never had to do so much work at home. Her mother often asked her to carry the peg bag into the garden when she was putting the washing on the line; and she had torn up newspapers into squares for the toilet, but never had she had to do all the things she had done that day. *And why couldn't she go to school?* she asked herself.

At seven o'clock she again climbed into her little bed, exhausted. *Why couldn't she go to school? Why wasn't Mrs Jones very friendly? After all, she had helped her all day.*

Mrs Jones was a rather pasty looking woman, with mousy brown hair, and a rather prominent nose. She couldn't be called nice looking. No, Margaret thought she was rather plain. Mrs Jones wasn't lazy, but she made sure everybody in the house did a fair share of the work. All the children had their jobs, but as Margaret wasn't family it seemed that Mrs Jones was making her do a great deal more than anyone else. While Margaret was cleaning and polishing Mrs Jones was often sitting mending socks and trousers. There was always a lot of washing each day, and washing had to be ironed. Mrs Jones would heat the two irons that permanently sat in the hearth. She would lift them and put them on a stand that swung over the fire, to get hot. Sometimes she put them on the range in the kitchen. Oh no, Mrs Jones was not lazy, but she treated Margaret like a maid.

When Margaret got into bed on the third night, she noticed how uncomfortable the bed was. It was only just off the floor. How she missed her nice bed at home, and her lovely dolly, Megan. She cuddled Mr Growler tightly, and soon fell asleep.

*

The other children helped at the weekend, when there was no school; and the only thing Margaret looked forward to was going to Sunday School on Sunday afternoons.

On Sundays, lunch in the Jones' household meant a large dinner mostly made up of potatoes and cabbage and very little meat. Margaret gradually became accustomed to eating this large meal in the middle of the day, instead of the bread and dripping they usually ate all week.

After lunch Jane would gather the six children including Margaret, all dressed in their Sunday best clothes, and accompany them to the local Chapel. Jane had firm instructions from her mother to look after them all and not to return until tea time, which was usually about 5 o'clock, because Sunday afternoons were rest time for herself and their father, who would spend the time in bed. These instructions appeared to be very firm, and Jane ensured that the children played in the park, or went for long walks in all sorts of weathers, and would not arrive home until ten minutes to five, just in time to lay the table for tea.

*

As the weeks passed Margaret became more and more unhappy. Why couldn't she go home? How long did she have to stay here with these people? No one told her. She never heard from her mother. She knew her name and address were written on the label she had attached to her gas mask.

One day she decided she must write to her mother. She had never written a letter before, but she could write some easy words. Surely Mummy would come and get her? She must let her mother know how unhappy she was.

When she was putting away the needle and cotton she had been using one day, she found a piece of paper and an envelope in a drawer.

She sneaked upstairs to her bedroom and carefully wrote the envelope, copying the address from the label on her gas mask. She took out the piece of paper and wrote in big letters:

Dear Mummy,
                I want to come home,
                        I don't like it,
                                Love   Margaret.

She folded the piece of paper, and put it into the envelope. She then sealed it and hid it under her pillow.

She found a stamp, but the next problem was how to post it.

She remembered that there had been a post box on the side of the road, on the way to the Chapel, but she would have to cross the busy road. The only time she went out without Mrs Jones was on Sundays.

The next Sunday she took the letter with her in her pocket, but although she passed the post box, she did not have the opportunity to cross the road to post the letter. She couldn't tell Jane about the letter. She took it home again.

The following Sunday, on their way back from Chapel, Jane decided to take the children to the park on the other side of the road, and crossed over some time before they passed the post box.

They crossed over, Margaret becoming excited, and as they walked along, she started to fall behind the others. She couldn't believe her luck.

As they neared the post box Margaret soon realised she would never be able to reach it. It was high up on a post. She went into the park with the others, walking right round the lake. She could feel the envelope in her pocket. Oh, how could she post the letter if she couldn't reach the box?

* * *

Chapter 4

As they left the park, Margaret still lagged behind. They passed the letter box, and as they did so she pulled out the letter, and as she was looking up a lady came up behind her and said, 'Can't you reach dear, here, let me.' She took the letter from the child's hand, and in a trice had posted it. She couldn't believe her luck, she smiled at the lady, thanked her and ran to join the others, who had walked on, and had not seen what had happened.

Elizabeth chided her. 'Come on slowcoach, keep up with us or you'll get lost.' Margaret didn't care. She had posted the letter!

*

Days passed, and nothing happened. Days turned to weeks. There was no letter from her mother, nor had her mother ever come to fetch her. She remembered John having told her that when things were not right when he had been staying in Maidenhead, their mother had gone to Maidenhead to sort things out. *Oh, why didn't she come and see that she was unhappy?*

Things went from bad to worse. Mrs Jones kept telling her off for being slow. Elizabeth kept taunting her. 'You will brush my hair for me each day before I go to school, I can't reach the back properly,' and 'If you don't tidy my bedroom I will tell Mummy, and she will punish you.'

So in her spare time she did Elizabeth's bidding. She was always afraid of being told off by Mrs Jones. One day when she had dropped a plate, and broken it, whilst putting it away, Mrs Jones had scolded her. 'We can't afford for you to break plates,' she had raved, 'you'll go to bed with no dinner . . . it costs enough to feed you as it is.'

Margaret had sobbed, and said she was sorry, but she was still sent upstairs when the family sat down to dinner. She sat on her little bed and told Mr Growler all about it, tears flowed down her face, she was so hungry.

Fortunately, Jane realised what had happened, and being the kind-hearted girl she was, she made up a plate of sandwiches after she had washed up, and took them upstairs to their bedroom without her parents knowing. She sat and put her arm around Margaret and told her not to worry, it would all have blown over by the morning.

The weather started to get colder. Her birthday in October had come and gone, and it was now November. It was cold and windy. It never seemed to stop raining and it was very cold in the scullery, unless the boiler was alight.

*

Some three weeks after Margaret had posted the letter to her mother, and she had given up all hope of hearing from her, there was a knock on the front door one Tuesday afternoon.

Mrs Jones answered the door, to find a tall man with sandy hair, which was beginning to grey, standing on the doorstep. He had a pair of bicycle clips in his hand, as well as a sort of brief case, which looked more like a satchel.

'Mrs Jones?' he enquired.

'Yes, that's right,' she replied.

He introduced himself as Mr Green, the Evacuation Welfare Officer. Margaret, who was standing beside Mrs Jones, saw her face change.

'How do you do,' he went on, 'I have called to see Margaret, to see how she has settled in.'

Mrs Jones invited him into the sitting room, and asked if he would like a cup of tea.

'That will be nice, thank you,' he replied.

Mrs Jones took off her pinny, and turning to Margaret said, 'Go and brush your hair, and wash your hands, and then you can come and see Mr Green, he wants to talk to you.' She said it so nicely to the child it took a minute for it to sink in. Mr Green wanted to talk to her.

Margaret was not sure what this man could want to talk to her about. He appeared to be a nice man, and he smiled at her as she turned and raced off to the scullery to wash her hands. Jim had brought in a wooden box which was kept under the sink, so that she could reach the tap. Jim was quite nice really. Then she ran upstairs to brush her hair, as she had been instructed.

Mrs Jones, who had gone into the scullery, put the kettle on, and then went back into the sitting room to join Mr Green. She hadn't been expecting anyone from the authorities to call.

'Margaret has settled well, Mr Green,' she told him. 'She is no trouble really.'

'I am pleased to hear it,' he said. 'Er . . . Mrs Jones, while we are alone, can you tell me if there is any reason why Margaret is not going to school. I checked with the school your youngest children go to, and find she has not been registered.'

Mrs Jones smiled at him and said, 'Margaret was very shy and not happy about going, so I said she could stay at home with me for the time being, until she wanted to go.'

'I see,' he said.

Mrs Jones went off to make the tea when the kettle started to whistle. Mr Green did not see how uneasy she was. She came back loaded with a tray with three cups and saucers, and a plate of biscuits. Margaret came downstairs and joined them. Mrs Jones poured out the tea, and handed round the plate of biscuits. Mr Green smiled benevolently at Margaret, who immediately became shy of him. She wasn't used to a cup and saucer, and she was scared she would spill her tea, either down her dress or over the carpet.

'Margaret, I have told Mrs Jones that I would like to talk to you on your own for a few minutes, is that all right?' he asked.

Her eyes were enormous, but she nodded her head. Mrs Jones looked anxious.

He talked for some time with Mrs Jones about the weather, and asked how her husband was, until the tea was finished. She then picked up the tray and went off into the kitchen. She closed the door behind her.

Margaret sat quietly, staring at Mr Green.

'Now Margaret, let me firstly tell you, I have been asked to call and see you because you had written to your mother telling her you were unhappy here, and you wanted to go home, is that right?'

Margaret nodded. *Thank goodness her mother had received her letter,* she thought. Her heart started beating. *I'm going home!*

'Are you not happy here?' he asked.

She shook her head.

'Tell me why?'

Margaret started to cry. The tears rolled down her cheeks. He took out a large handkerchief from his jacket pocket and held it out to her.

'Here my dear, wipe your eyes,' he said kindly. 'Now tell me my dear, what is the matter? Mrs Jones seems very nice.'

As her sobbing abated, gradually she choked out how unhappy she was. She told him she missed her mother and her brother.

Mr Green said, 'There are lots of children here in North Wales who are missing their families my dear, you are not alone.'

Margaret continued to weep quietly, and then knowing this was her opportunity to go home, she told Mr Green how she was made to eat her meals in the scullery, and how she wasn't allowed to go to school: staying here all day and doing lots of work around the house.

Mr Green listened, fearing that the child was telling him the truth. Mrs Jones was obviously keeping her home from school for her own ends.

He asked Margaret if she would like to go to school. Her eyes lit up. 'Ooh, yes please,' she said. He continued to talk with her about her mother and told her that there was no way at present that she could visit her, because of the war, which was still raging in London. Margaret was devastated. Mr Green had been very kind, but quite specific, she couldn't go home, and her mother could not come and visit her.

Mr Green called Mrs Jones back into the sitting room, and explained that there had been a change of plan, and Margaret was to be moved later that day. That he had wanted to make sure for himself how Margaret was first, but he was positive that a move would be in her best interests.

She would be going to stay with a Mrs Perie in Victoria Road. He went on to explain that some of the children were being moved to more spacious accommodation now that things had settled down, and Mrs Perie could offer Margaret a bedroom of her own.

Mrs Jones said nothing. Her face was a picture of disbelief. He thanked Mrs Jones for caring for Margaret, but said he was aware that she had six children of her own, and things could not be easy for her.

Mrs Jones looked very cross, but said in a pleasant voice, 'Well, if it is for the best, but we'll miss the money we are paid for caring for Margaret. If you have any more children please consider us.'

Mr Green assured her the organisation would keep their names on the register. He said, 'I'll come back later today, around 4 o'clock to collect her, if you can help Margaret pack her things together I would be grateful.'

'Certainly, I'll have her ready.'

He rose to go. He smiled at the child and said, 'I'll see you later young lady, and I'll take you to Victoria Road and introduce you to Mrs Perie. I'm sure you will like her.'

After he had left, Mrs Jones sent her upstairs to put her things into her case. 'Come down afterwards and I'll give you the clothes I have just washed,' she said. As she turned round she continued, 'I cannot understand why you are being moved. What did you say to Mr Green?'

'Nothing,' Margaret replied, and fled upstairs. The child was not sure either really. She had hoped she was going home, now she was going somewhere else. She was not sure if this was best. On the other hand she didn't like living here with the Jones family, and Mr Green had intimated she could go to school.

With her suitcase packed and Mr Growler safely tucked under her arm, she waited for the other children to come in from school. But before they arrived Mr Green once more knocked on the front door, just before 4 o'clock, and Margaret was invited to follow him outside. He took hold of her suitcase. His bicycle had been replaced by a little black Austin 7 car. He helped her into the front seat, and then got in himself after he had turned a handle at the front of the car. Mrs Jones did not wave goodbye, she went straight back indoors and shut the door.

*

Margaret had never been in a motor car before. It was a new experience. The car started up the road, and turned out of

Salisbury Road and left into Talbot Road. Mrs Jones used to walk her along here towards the shops each week. The car continued to the bottom and turned right. They crossed a junction and she saw the road was called Fairy Road. *What a lovely name,* she thought. At the end they went round a roundabout and turned into Victoria Road.

Mr Green told Margaret, 'You will like Mrs Perie, she is a very kind lady; I am sure you will love having your own bedroom as well. Mrs Perie lives quite near to the school.' Halfway along the road Mr Green stopped the car outside No. 23.

'Here we are, I'll come round and open the door for you.' He walked round the front of the car and opened the car door for her, then he leant inside and brought out her suitcase, which had been on the backseat.

When she stepped out and looked at the house, it was to see that it was nicely painted in white with a royal blue front door. The curtains looked pretty, and there were nice flowers in the front garden. They walked up to the front door, and Mr Green rapped the knocker, and very soon the door was opened.

An elderly lady stood there; she was very old to Margaret, but had a lovely smile. Her silver grey hair was tied back into a knot at the nape of her neck. She had lovely eyes, and how kind she looked.

In the space of a few seconds she came out and said, 'Hello, so you are Margaret, I have been so looking forward to you coming, I have heard so much about you from Mr Green. Do come in my dear.' She turned and said, 'Do come in Mr Green, I'll pop the kettle on.'

They followed her in. 'You must meet my daughter Pamela,' she said to Margaret. She called out, 'Pamela, they are here.'

A younger version of Mrs Perie came down the stairs. She seemed middle aged, but was probably in her thirties. She also had a lovely smile, and beautiful curly brown hair, which hung down to her shoulders. She was taller than her mother, and rather plump. 'So you are coming to stay with us?' she asked, 'that is lovely; let me take your suitcase upstairs and show you your room.'

Margaret followed her upstairs. Pamela had taken the case from Mr Green. She was conscious that her best dress, which she had on, had black shoe polish on the skirt.

As she was shown into the room that was to be hers, she couldn't believe her eyes. It was lovely. Pretty frilled curtains were hanging at the window, and a proper bed with a pretty cover. A chair and table stood in the corner, and on the dressing table was a little vase with some chrysanthemums in. They smelt lovely too. As she passed the windows she noticed the room overlooked the back garden. She could see a lawn with borders full of flowers and shrubs round it. At the bottom grew lots of vegetables. But her eyes sparkled when she saw the garden swing.

Pamela took the things out of her case and put them in the chest of drawers. She showed Margaret the little bathroom along the landing, and gave her a towel and flannel from the airing cupboard for her own use.

'We hope you will like it here, we are not used to having children about, but it should be fun.'

They went downstairs, and Mrs Perie gave Margaret some orange squash, and everyone else had cups of tea. A cake-stand was offered round, with little cakes on, and a gingerbread man for her.

Oh how nice, she thought. Her eyes sparkled once more.

After lots of chat, Mr Green got up to leave. Margaret had listened to him telling Mrs Perie how unhappy she had been since coming to Wrexham, and how she had managed to write to her mother, which had alerted the authorities. He said he would call in a few days to see if everything was all right, and promised Margaret that he would write to her mother, and tell her where she was now staying.

That evening she enjoyed a lovely dinner of chicken, which was followed by ice cream. It was sheer luxury to sit at the table in the dining room with the two ladies. Both ladies chatted to her and asked her lots of questions about her family, and she had been able to say how she missed her mother, and John, and Bobbie the dog. She said she also missed her favourite doll, Megan, who had been too big to bring with her.

Afterwards they sat round the fire and listened to the wireless. Pamela went out into the kitchen and filled a stone hot water bottle, and took it up and placed it in her little bed.

That night she slept peacefully in her lovely comfy bed, which was nice and warm. The clothes she had on when she arrived magically disappeared, and a fresh blouse and skirt had been put out for her to put on when she woke the next morning. There were also clean white socks and a warm cardigan. She didn't know where they had come from, they were not hers, but they were nice, and fitted her well.

It was so nice to wash in the bathroom, which had a little sink, before putting on her new clothes. Pamela came into her bedroom and helped her brush her hair, before they went downstairs for breakfast. There was a treat in store. They had scrambled eggs on toast, and Margaret had a glass of milk.

Pamela said, 'We will go for a walk to the school, it is just down the road, and arrange for you to start there tomorrow.'

So at half past nine they set off. It was a nice day, but rather cold. There was a nip in the air. Margaret was not concerned for she felt nice and warm in her new cardigan, as well as her coat.

They approached the school, and went through the big gate, walking across the playground and into the main building.

Pamela spoke to a lady at the office and explained that Margaret needed to start school. Margaret, however, was looking all about her. It was a very old school with high ceilings. The parquet floors were highly polished, and there were lots of pictures and writing pinned to the walls. Some children passed her, and she felt very nervous.

Another lady showed them round. They went through the school hall where some children were barefoot and doing PE, then along a corridor to a classroom where Margaret was introduced to Miss Hughes, who was to be her teacher. It was agreed she would start the following day at 9 o'clock.

It was as she was leaving the main hall that she saw Elizabeth Jones, who stared at her. Pamela took hold of Margaret's hand and they went outside. So this was the school that Toby and Elizabeth Jones went to.

'I think we will go to the shops and get you some more clothes, you have hardly anything with you,' Pamela said.

So some two hours later they returned to 23 Victoria Road laden with lots of paper bags full of jumpers, skirts, socks, and a lovely new best dress. It was beautiful, a pretty plum colour, and right across the front was delicate smocking in pretty colours. It also had an adorable Peter Pan collar. Pamela had also bought two warm liberty bodices with little rubber buttons, saying they would keep her warm during the winter.

One bag contained some crayons, colouring books, and a lovely doll, who she immediately called Jane.

On their return Mrs Perie had lunch ready for them. A bowl of hot home made soup, followed by tiny sandwiches and sausage rolls. Margaret was still excited from having been to the school, and also her shopping expedition with Pamela. She showed Mrs Perie all the things that had been purchased.

She raced upstairs after lunch and put all her new clothes away, and then sat at the dining table, crayoning one of the pictures in her new book. How she liked Pamela, and how kind Mrs Perie was. Later in life she was to remember the kindness shown to her, and the feeling of never wanting to leave.

* * *

Chapter 5

The following morning she dressed in the grey skirt and white blouse which had been bought for her the day before. Pamela took her to the school gate and collected her at 4 o'clock. Margaret recalled how she had loved going to school at home, though her mother wouldn't be working in this school.

She was soon to learn that attending school in North Wales was to be totally different to her school in Upminster.

On this, the first morning, she put her coat in the cloakroom, as she had been told, and went into the classroom. The first problem she encountered hit her like a thunderbolt. They all spoke a funny language. She couldn't understand what the other children were saying. Mrs Hughes soon enlightened her, and said a lot of the children only spoke Welsh, that some spoke some English, and some could speak English quite fluently. She went on to say that many of the lessons were all spoken in Welsh, and most of the hymns and songs were also sung in Welsh.

Although Margaret had noticed that most of the people she had so far met, including the Jones family, had a strange lilt to their speech, they all spoke very good English. However was she going to understand the lessons, when she didn't know the language?

The second problem which beset her was Elizabeth Jones. Margaret had seen Toby, Elizabeth's younger brother, briefly in the playground, and he had smiled and said hello. But Elizabeth immediately snubbed her and started telling the other children around her that Margaret was an orphan, and that her own mother had taken the child in, from the kindness of her heart, and all the thanks she had received was Margaret telling the Welfare Officer that she didn't like it there. The other children had jeered her, and called her "vacci"; they certainly stayed away from her and would not let her join in their playground games. She soon learnt that Elizabeth had poisoned the minds of most of the children, and knew she was now unpopular.

Over the next few weeks, Elizabeth continued to taunt her, calling her names. Margaret's respite came each day when Pamela came to collect her from school, and she was able to forget how nasty Elizabeth Jones was to her, until she went to school the next day.

Mrs Perie soon noticed Margaret had something on her mind when she came in from school, and quietly talked to her, and discovered what the problems were. Mrs Perie set out to teach Margaret some Welsh, and each evening they spent a little time with the language. Margaret was quick to learn, and this impressed Mrs Hughes, her teacher.

As far as the children jeering at her was concerned, she was not sure what to do, so she talked to Pamela about it. Unbeknown to Margaret Pamela went to the school and saw Miss Hughes, and told her what was happening and how unhappy it was making Margaret.

She never understood how, but gradually the other children started to talk to her, and let her join in their games. This did not include Elizabeth Jones or her cronies, who still avoided her.

After only three short weeks, just before Christmas she went down with a heavy cold. Mrs Perie decided that she should not go to school. She spent a morning in bed, with Pamela bringing her breakfast, of a boiled egg with soldiers and a cup of hot chocolate, on a tray. It was lovely. Later that morning, once the fire was alight, she was taken downstairs in a blanket and sat in front of the fire. Mrs Perie made her a beaker of hot lemon and honey. How she loved these ladies, they really spoilt her, and cared for her even better than her own mother. Mrs Perie rubbed her chest with camphorated oil, which made her feel lovely and warm, and eased her breathing. It also gave an extra opportunity to learn a little more Welsh.

*

Margaret loved her life at Victoria Road. Pamela was always fun and amused her greatly. At weekends she took the child out to see places in the vicinity, and one day took her on a long journey to Rhyl. It was a seaside town; Margaret had never seen the sea. The good lady told her that she wanted to get some small presents for Christmas, and there were much better shops in Rhyl. Pamela also took Margaret to a cafeteria, where they sat and drank milk shakes and ate hot scones, with lots of jam and cream. Ooo... what a treat!

It had been quite a nice warm sunny day, but not warm enough to paddle on the beach, although there were one or two brave souls holding up their skirts and paddling at the water's edge. Pamela thought this would not be a good idea. Pamela had bought some little packages, which she said were to go under the Christmas Tree.

Christmas was great fun, and Mrs Perie made a lovely Christmas Pudding, just like her own mother made.

After breakfast, they all got ready and went the short distance to Poyser Street, where the big church was. There was a warm welcome for Mrs Perie and Pamela, and lots of people said hello to her. She had been with them to church before, but this was Christmas and everyone was wishing each other a lovely day and a Happy New Year. The vicar had stood in the pulpit and prayed that the war would soon come to an end. *Yes,* she thought, *it would be nice,* then she could go home to see her mother and John, but she knew she wasn't too unhappy about this, she liked living with these two kind ladies.

Later that day, they opened their presents. She was so excited. Pamela had bought her a little pale blue zipped case, and inside was a manicure set, with little soft buffers for her nails as well as scissors and nail file. Pamela told her she would show her how to care for her nails later on. Mrs Perie had made her a little woollen bobble hat, which came right down over her ears to keep them warm, it was blue to match her coat. Then Pamela gave her a small parcel which had come in the post. A pair of bedsocks from her mother. Her mother had made them for her. She hadn't forgotten her. Oh, she felt so happy!

The next few months were cold and there was lots of snow and ice. She couldn't go out and play on the swing, but she did make a snowman, who took some two weeks to melt.

She started to go to Sunday School, which she enjoyed each week, and joined the choir. Her school work gradually improved and she started to excel at arithmetic and English, and she now knew the Welsh National Anthem by heart. Margaret was good at sports, and soon played in the school teams for rounders and netball.

In April, she received a letter from John, it was lovely to hear from him, but the news, that Bobbie the dog had died, made her cry. Pamela consoled her and said that he may have been ill or hurt, and that he would now be in heaven, where he would be quite happy. This cheered her a little. John also told her that their mother had met a man called Ted, and Ted often came to the house and took their mother out. *What would mother want with a strange man?* she wondered.

Every day Margaret listened to the little wireless. The war raged on. Mrs Perie liked Mr Churchill, who was the

Prime Minister, and doted on every word he said. She was such a gentle lady, but she often called the Germans all sorts of names, especially Hitler. She called him a "Dictator", though Margaret had no idea what that meant.

Mrs Perie became most excited one day when the man on the wireless, reading the news, said, "The RAF have bombed the Ruhr Dam in Germany, and the mission was successful".

'Oh, how wonderful,' she seemed overjoyed. 'Give them a taste of their own medicine.'

'Does that mean we have won the war?' Margaret asked.

'Not quite dear, but it will give them something to think about,' she replied. Margaret hugged the thought to herself that Hitler might have been drowned.

The summer progressed, and many things seemed to indicate that the war was coming to a close. But the war never ended.

Margaret worked hard at school, and enjoyed her Sundays at the church, whether she was singing in the choir or attending the services, which were so interesting. She liked the vicar immensely, and he took a lot of notice of her, she had no idea why.

*

September moved on to October. It would be her birthday soon. She would be eight years old. She would then be older than Elizabeth Jones by some few days. She was determined to tell her so when she saw her. She was not frightened of the child any more. Safely living with Mrs Perie and Pamela at Victoria Road, she had nothing to fear, especially as she was well in favour with Miss Hughes at school.

On the 22nd October, just one day before her birthday, Mrs Perie told her she had to prepare the spare bedroom, as she was expecting a visitor. Someone was coming to stay for a day or two, providing they could arrange transport. Margaret was curious, but said nothing. *Who could it be?* she thought.

She helped carry the sheets and pillowcases into the spare room, and helped Mrs Perie make up the bed. 'See if you can find a few nice flowers in the garden, and I'll put them in a vase,' she said to Margaret.

She went out into the back garden, that she loved so much, and cut some pretty chrysanthemums, all gold and mauve. She knew they would match the bedspread. But who was coming?

Mrs Perie was busy in the kitchen for the rest of the morning baking little scones and cakes, and putting meat and vegetables into the big cooking pot. This she placed into the slow oven. Margaret loved it when she did this, as all day the lovely aroma of food would permeate the house.

Mrs Perie suggested that she put on her best plum coloured dress after lunch, and she herself changed into a lovely lilac coloured dress, which suited her so well. The elderly lady looked so beautiful, with her fine white hair and green eyes. How Margaret loved this wonderful lady, who was so kind to her.

She had just taken the little vase of flowers upstairs to put on the dressing table in the spare bedroom, when she looked out of the window and saw a car draw up outside. She knew that car so well. Mr Green stepped out. Surely he wasn't coming to stay! He walked round the car, and out stepped a lady. Margaret stared; she couldn't believe it. It was her mother!

She ran down the stairs as fast as her legs could carry her. 'Mrs Perie,' she shouted, 'it is my mother, she has come for me.' Margaret tugged at her arm, bidding her to hurry and answer the front door.

Mrs Perie said, 'Margaret dear, it is true your mother is coming to visit you. I didn't tell you before, because there was a possibility that she would not be able to afford the fare to come; she has wanted to come for some time to see you were all right, and your birthday was the ideal time.' She went on 'Your mother will be staying for two nights, but the war is still on, and it is too dangerous for you to go back to London just yet.'

Margaret listened, but she was excited.

Mrs Perie opened the front door, and Margaret ran down the front path and dashed into her mother's arms.

'Mummy, Mummy,' she cried. Tears of joy flowed down her cheeks. She was crying and laughing all at the same time.

Her mother swept her up, and kissed her. 'Oh, how lovely to see you, I have been so worried about you.' She went on, 'Mr Green has been so kind and helpful. I was so pleased to hear you have been moved. I could tell from your letter how unhappy you were, I knew something was wrong. Mr Green wrote and said you had settled in well with Mrs Perie, I hope you like it here?'

'Oh yes, Mummy, Mrs Perie and Pamela take care of me,' but she didn't explain how spoilt she was by the two ladies.

She told her mother how Mrs Perie cooked lovely meals for her, and would sit and read interesting stories to her. Her favourite was *Little Women*, by Louisa M Allcott, and also *Jane Eyre* by Charlotte Brontë. She would help her read her school books and had taught her to converse in Welsh. This had helped so much at school.

And she told how Pamela had taught her to look after her nails with the little manicure set. Pamela would sit and polish her nails with little soft pads of chamois leather, and of the many times Pamela would go out and spend her sweet ration on her. Yes, Mr Green had been right, the ladies were very kind.

Mr Green had, by now, extracted a case from the back seat of the car, and Mrs Perie came over and introduced herself to Mrs Trent saying, 'It is nice to meet you at last. Come into the sitting room, you must be tired after your long journey. I'll go and make some tea.' After a moment she continued, 'You are welcome to go upstairs and use the bathroom if you would like to wash your hands and face.' Mrs Trent took up the kind offer.

'Margaret, show your mother up to the bathroom, will you dear? I'll go and sort out the tea. Do sit down Mr Green, I won't be a moment.'

'This way Mummy,' Margaret raced ahead, 'I'll show you my bedroom.' She skipped up the stairs, followed by her mother. Margaret gave her no chance to go to the bathroom, but took her straight to her own bedroom.

'Look at my room Mummy, and my new clothes,' she said. 'And my new dolly that Pamela bought me, I call her Jane. Where I lived before Jane was so nice, so I called my dolly after her.' She couldn't stop talking!

In the end Mrs Trent, who was taking everything in, and agreeing everything was very nice, had to say, 'It's lovely dear, but can I now just slip to the bathroom, there will be lots of time for us to chat.'

Margaret preceded her mother along the landing, and showed her the bathroom. Then she dashed downstairs. She skipped down the passageway, and went straight into the kitchen and asked Mrs Perie if she could carry the tea tray.

'Well dear, thank you, but I am afraid it will be too heavy for you, but you can carry the cake stand and put it on the coffee table for me.' She took the cake stand, piled high with cakes and scones that Mrs Perie had made that morning, and went into the sitting room, where Mr Green, being the gentleman he was, stood up as she entered, and smiled at her.

'I can see you are very helpful around the house, my dear,' he said to her. She was overwhelmed with gratitude. Mr Green was always so kind to her. He had taken her away from that awful family and found her this lovely place to stay, and now he had brought her mother to see her. She was so grateful to him. He had told her on his last visit that he had to visit lots of children in the area, and ensure they were happy and well cared for. He really was a nice man.

It didn't take Mrs Trent long to realise that Margaret was very well cared for and happy where she was staying.

Mr Green reiterated what Mrs Perie had previously told her, that the bombs were still falling on London, and that it would not be safe for her to go home yet. Mr Green promised her that as soon as it was, arrangements would be made for her to return. Margaret felt that was all right, after all she had her mother there, and she liked Mrs Perie and Pamela. And it couldn't be long before the war ended. She remembered that Mrs Perie had told her just a few days ago that the Germans had surrendered at Stalingrad.

Margaret treasured every moment over the next two days with her mother, and showed her all the things she had, and how Mrs Perie had taught her to sew, and her attempts at embroidery.

Her mother asked her about the letter which she had received, and what had been wrong when she stayed with the Jones family.

Margaret told her how unhappy she had been, and especially that she had not been allowed to go to school, Mrs Trent was shocked to learn how much housework she had been expected to do, and by the way the family had treated her, especially Mrs Jones and Elizabeth. Margaret told her about having to eat her meals on her own in the scullery, but more importantly, she told her mother how she missed being with her and John. They laughed together about how she had come to post the letter. It seemed funny now.

Mrs Trent was so pleased she had contacted the authorities. She was also grateful to the local vicar at St Lawrence's Church, for paying her fare so that she could come and see for herself. She had been surprised when the vicar had told her that collections had been taken especially to reunite parents with their children.

She had had lots of sleepless nights, worrying about her young daughter. Feeling guilty that she had sent her to North Wales with the other children, even though she knew she was safer in Wales than in London.

Mrs Trent liked Pamela very much, but was upset to learn from her that she was concerned for Mrs Perie's health. She felt her mother was a little frail, and had been uncertain about whether Margaret coming to stay would tax her strength. But she wholeheartedly agreed that her mother loved having Margaret to fuss over, and that the child was no trouble. She emphasised that Margaret was a delightful little girl, and hoped she could stay for the rest of the war. Mrs Trent hoped so too.

Pamela Perie escorted them about the town, allowing Mrs Trent to see the school Margaret attended, and where she went to Sunday School, then into the little town, and down past the park with the lake. It was beginning to get quite cold. Mrs Trent had brought some hand knitted socks and a long scarf for Margaret. They were nice and warm.

On the second day, Margaret rose early. She knew her mother would be leaving the next day. She must make the most of today.

After breakfast, they set out for a walk together. Her mother took the opportunity to tell Margaret that the family had moved from Upminster, and they were now living in a hotel in Richmond.

'Is John living there too?' Margaret asked.

'Oh yes dear, he is still at college, and travels each day by train.'

'I miss John, Mummy.'

'I know dear, but he must finish his education so that he can get a good job when he leaves, otherwise he might have been sent off like you.'

'John wrote and told me that you have a friend called Ted?'

Her mother looked startled for a moment, then recovering, she said, 'I didn't know John had written to you.' Then, 'Yes, I have got a friend called Ted, in fact he is the Assistant Manager of the Hotel where we are staying at the moment. You would like him, Margaret.

She was not sure she would like him, he could never be like Daddy, how she missed Daddy. No, she didn't think she would like him one little bit.

Perhaps it was his fault that her mother had moved from Upminster, and the lovely house she had looked forward to going back to. Now she would be going back to some strange place. She felt torn between the tranquillity of the present situation, and this unknown place where her mother now lived.

All too soon the two days flew by, and it was time for Mrs Trent to leave. Margaret did not want her mother to go. Mr Green dutifully arrived in his little car at about 8 o'clock in the morning to collect her mother and take her to the station. Mr Green pulled Margaret to one side and said, 'It should not be long before you can go back to London, do not worry yourself; and you have Mrs Perie and Pamela who will take care of you. You'll be all right.'

Margaret nodded. Yes, he was right. All the same she was crying profusely as his car drove away.

Her mother was gone.

* * *

Chapter 6

Later that evening, as she was getting ready for bed she felt sad her mother had gone. She knew it was a long way. She also knew that she really loved Mr Green. He had been so kind to her. Little did she know that many years later she would want to have a job just like his, caring about children – the seed was sown.

*

Over the next two weeks, two things became obvious to Margaret.

The first was that Pamela spent a lot more time away from the house, and appeared to come back very happy. She had never appeared to go to work regularly, like a lot of people did during the week. She knew she often went to town and did the shopping after taking her to school, and that she was involved in helping the local vicar. She arranged the flowers at the local church, and attended choir practice, where she sang soprano.

Pamela started to go out more regularly every afternoon, as well as in the evenings, and at weekends. She asked Mrs Perie where Pamela went when curiosity got the better of her.

'Well dear, the government has decided that part time work is compulsory for women aged between 18 and 45, so Pamela has to work some afternoons at the local factory. You see, a lot of the men have had to go to the war, and the workers are needed to enable things to keep going.'

'Oh, I see,' Margaret replied. But that did not explain why Pamela went out at evenings and weekends. She was beginning to miss her company.

Then there was the man who used to come back with her, who was about the same age, usually bidding him farewell at the front door. On two occasions Mrs Perie had invited him in for a cup of tea, and chatted to him.

The second thing she noticed was that many people came to call and brought little gifts for Mrs Perie. A few fresh eggs, sometimes some apples, or some cheese. Lots of people seemed to know her and to like her. Also, Mrs Perie didn't get up each day until nearly lunchtime, and often nodded in her chair in front of the fire.

She was later to learn that Mrs Perie's husband had been the local vicar before the Reverend Hewitt, though she was oblivious to this information at the time.

All three of them went to the local church on Sundays to the family service. Margaret felt very proud to stand near the front of the church, between Mrs Perie and Pamela. Just recently Mrs Perie had missed going to church, preferring to sit quietly at home, although always wanting to know any news of interest on their return.

So the weeks flew by. Christmas came and went. It had been fun helping Pamela set up the little Christmas tree, and making a little fairy for the top. Pamela had cooked the Christmas dinner. It was the first time Margaret had ever tasted goose. Pamela's friend James came for Christmas dinner, and carved the bird. Mrs Perie seemed happy to just sit and be waited on.

Margaret quite liked James. Although she had reservations at first she could see he was a nice man, who made Pamela laugh a lot, and Mrs Perie made a great fuss of him.

She never received a card from her mother, the only one she had was from Mrs Perie and Pamela. She had made them one at school, and had given both ladies little lavender bags, to hang in their wardrobes.

Pamela had bought her some pretty writing paper and envelopes so that she could write to her mother, and Mrs Perie had given her a little book illustrating all the birds. They had for some time been feeding the birds in the garden, as it was so cold. On the wireless Bing Crosby crooned *White Christmas* for the first time. In January Mrs Perie stayed in bed for quite a few days with a bad cold. Pamela said she was afraid her mother might catch pneumonia, as it was so cold. But within a week she seemed better and was able to come downstairs.

Margaret was warm and cosy in this nice house, and almost forgot at times that she had her own family back in London. She liked school, and even Elizabeth Jones had stopped taunting her. She also enjoyed the occasional outing with Pamela.

*

Then, on a fateful day in March, her pleasant world came to an end. She came home from school to find strange people in the house. The lady who lived across the road answered the door to her, and told her to come in. Pamela had not met her from school as she did on Mondays. Dr Roberts, the local GP, was coming down the stairs carrying his little bag.

'Hello Margaret,' he said, 'I'm afraid you can't go upstairs for the moment. Come into the kitchen.' She could hear someone crying upstairs. She followed Dr Roberts into the kitchen. She had only met him once before, just before Christmas, Pamela had taken her to see him because she had a sore throat, and he had given her some nice lemony medicine.

'Where is everybody?' she asked him.

'I am afraid this is going to be sad news for you. I am sorry to tell you that Mrs Perie died today. As you know she was an elderly lady, and has not been very strong lately.'

Margaret was distraught. She didn't really understand, except she suddenly realised it was Pamela she had heard crying upstairs when she came in. She burst into tears.

She thought, *Mrs Perie couldn't have died, she had been fine this morning before she went to school. She had been up, and waved bye bye to her. No, it could not be true.*

Dr Roberts however, assured her that, sadly, it was. He stayed for a while, and the lady across the road, Mrs Rees, made some tea. There was a lot of commotion on the stairs, and then Pamela, her face swollen from crying, came into the kitchen.

'Oh Margaret, I am so going to miss my mother. She was such a lovely lady,' she said.

Margaret said, 'Can I go and see her,' still sure she would find Mrs Perie sitting up in bed.

Pamela put her arms around Margaret and said, 'I am afraid they have taken her to the Chapel of Rest, dear, you won't be able to see her.'

Margaret was dumbfounded. So she had died. Just like her father had died when she was six.

Pamela and Margaret continued to sob when they were left alone, each consoling the other about their sad loss.

The funeral took place four days later, but Margaret was not allowed to attend. As it was Saturday, she had to stay with Mrs Rees at her house across the road. Mrs Rees was very nice, and Margaret didn't mind helping her spread lots of bread with margarine, while the good lady made up sandwiches for the funeral tea.

Later that day, she helped Pamela hand them out to lots of people she did not know, except the vicar, Rev Hewitt, and of course Mrs Rees. Some of the people she vaguely recognised, who had come to the house to see Mrs Perie and bring her things.

By 5 o'clock they all went away, leaving Pamela and Margaret alone, busy clearing up the plates, cups and saucers. Pamela spent a lot of time sitting and talking with Margaret. She didn't leave the child often, but the next two Saturdays Margaret went to stay with Mrs Rees, as Pamela had to see someone.

*

Some two weeks later, she returned home from school to find Mr Green's car outside the house. She was pleased, she hadn't seen him since her mother had visited. She ran up to the front door. Pamela let her in and suggested she go upstairs and change out of her school clothes, and then she could join them in the sitting room for tea.

Margaret raced upstairs. She liked Mr Green. Perhaps there was news of her going home.

On entering the lounge, Mr Green rose and said 'Hello Margaret, have you had a good day at school?'

She told him about the Policeman who came to the school and told the children not to talk to strange men, but to go straight home from school. She said she didn't know why. The men she knew were very nice. There was Mr Green, the Rev Hewitt, and Mr Rees across the road.

'Well I believe there has been a bit of trouble my dear, a man has been loitering in the area. I think you need to heed the policeman's warning,' he told her.

'Very well,' she replied.

She went on to tell him she had been top of the class at spelling that day. 'Very good, your teacher must be pleased with you,' he patted her on the shoulder. 'Come and sit next to me on the sofa.'

She sat down, and told him she missed Mrs Perie, helping her with her Welsh, and the lovely meals she used to cook.

'Well, Margaret, I am afraid I have a bit more bad news for you.'

Goodness, what else could there be?

'Well now, it is not bad news for Pamela.' He looked at Pamela, who smiled back at him.

'You see my dear, Pamela is going to get married.'

'Ooh, how lovely!' She turned to Pamela, 'Can I be a bridesmaid?'

Pamela smiled at her, came over and knelt down in front of her, taking her hand.

'Margaret, I would love to have you as a bridesmaid, but unfortunately we are only having a quick Registry Office wedding. You see James, my future husband, has to sail for America very soon, and I plan to go with him,' she explained.

'Where's America?' she asked.

Pamela told her, 'It is a long way across the sea. It will take many days to get there.'

'Can I come with you?' Margaret asked.

Pamela and Mr Green looked at each other. The room was very quiet. She looked from one to the other of them.

Mr Green once more looked across at Pamela, then said, 'I'm afraid you will not be able to go with Pamela and Mr Johnson. Pamela will be gone a long time, and she has to sort a lot of things out about this house. She will be giving up the tenancy next week.'

'Am I going home, Mr Green? she asked.

'No Margaret, that will not be possible, my child. The war is still not over. But I have found you another family home where you can stay until you can go home.'

'I don't want to go anywhere else, I like it here,' she wailed.

'I know my dear, it is upsetting, but I can assure you Mrs Hall seems very nice. The only problem is, you will have to change schools as she lives on the far side of Wrexham, so it would be too far for you to come to your present school.'

'I don't want to go anywhere,' she shouted.

Pamela, who had sat back in her chair, now got up again and came and sat on the arm of the sofa; she put her arm round Margaret's shoulders and said, 'I'll come with you to see Mrs Hall if you like, we could go with Mr Green tomorrow.'

Margaret started crying, and got up and ran out of the room and up to her bedroom. She threw herself on her bed and cried and cried.

Why did she lose everybody? First her father had died and left her, then she had been sent away from her mother and brother, who she needed so badly. Her lovely doll Megan was somewhere strange, probably missing her as much as she missed Megan. Then there was Bobbie the dog, who she couldn't cuddle. Mrs Perie had died, and now Pamela was leaving her.

Her world was in tatters. Not only would she have to leave this lovely house, but she had to change schools and her teacher, Miss Hughes.

A little while later she heard the front door close, and Pamela came up to her bedroom.

'Oh Margaret, I am sorry, please don't cry any more,' she said. 'I have asked Mr Green to come and collect us at 10 o'clock tomorrow morning. We will all go together to see Mrs Hall. Mr Green tells me there is another girl staying there, about your own age, her name is Betty. She will be company for you.' She went on, 'It won't be like the family you lived with before, Mr Green will see that you are happy where you are placed, and he will write and let me know how you are getting on.'

Margaret thought about this, and felt pacified a little. But that evening, she walked round the house, touching all the familiar things, with a lump in her throat.

There was the little chiming clock on the mantelpiece that she liked, and Mrs Perie's sewing basket, which contained all those pretty cottons and ribbons. The little wireless that played nice music, and the table she sat at for her meals.

As she went out into the garden she sighed as she sat on the swing and gently swung backwards and forwards. What a lovely garden, and all the lovely spring flowers were just coming up. Daffodils, crocuses and tulips, even though it was still bitterly cold.

Later, upstairs, she looked around her bedroom. The pretty covers on the dressing table trimmed with lace. The little pottery dishes she kept her hair slides in. The little vase of flowers always there, and her lovely bed. Mr Growler loved this bed. There he lay just inside the covers, all tucked up.

OH! How could she leave here?

This was home.

* * *

Chapter 7

The following morning, Pamela and Margaret set off promptly at 10 o'clock in Mr Green's car, and drove for some distance. They went towards the town centre first, through the High Street, and turned left into Chester Street. They passed the Memorial Hall where she had been introduced to Mr and Mrs Jones last year, and then turned right into Park Avenue. Mr Green crossed over Rhosnesni Lane, and turned into Maple Avenue, where he stopped the car.

They had stopped some way from the house, as there was a large expanse of grass in front of the houses. They walked across the grass, and up the garden path of 33 Maple Avenue. Their knock on the front door was answered by a rather plump middle-aged lady, who invited them all in. Margaret looked around her. Mrs Hall seemed pleasant enough when she took Margaret and Pamela upstairs to see where she was to sleep.

'Betty is at school at the moment, but you will be sharing this room with her,' she told the child.

It was a large room, and had two identical single beds in it, each against a wall. In between was a chest of drawers, which had a swivel mirror standing on the top. There was another chest of drawers on the other side of the room near the window, on top of which stood a large wash basin and jug. The two beds had identical cotton covers, and one bed had a doll lying across it.

Mrs Hall pointed to the second chest of drawers and said, 'This will be your chest of drawers. Plenty of room for all your things.' She turned to Pamela and said, 'I'm sure she will be comfortable, and Betty is a nice girl.' Pamela smiled at her.

They went downstairs. It wasn't as cosy as Mrs Perie's house. The furniture was rather tatty, but everything looked clean. There was an old Welsh dresser on the far wall, with plates and cups and saucers arranged on it. One particular armchair set near the fireplace looked very careworn, and into this sat Mrs Hall.

She followed Pamela through the kitchen and out into the garden. It was very long, but was mainly grass, with a few bushes that had been planted around the edges.

No nice pretty flowers that had lovely scent, like at Victoria Road. No nice swing. 'I don't know if I shall like it here,' she said to Pamela.

Pamela put her arm around the child and looked down at her. 'Margaret, you will have to give it time. Nowhere is the same, but Mr Green thought you would be happy here. I know you are missing Mother, so am I, but she won't be coming back. I miss her terribly my dear, but life moves on. Come on, let's join the others inside.'

They went back to the sitting room. Mrs Hall was telling Mr Green, 'Margaret can go to school with Betty each day; it is a long walk, but they are young. It doesn't take long.'

They sat for some time talking together. Pamela sat on a pouffe next to her, and Margaret sat quietly in one of the big armchairs, staring at Mrs Hall.

She wore a pinny just like Mrs Jones. Fear clutched her heart. She also wore lace up shoes like grannies did, and she never offered to make a cup of tea. But she seemed friendly enough. They kept asking her questions about things, but she was too nervous to reply. Eventually Pamela took her outside again and asked her how she felt. Margaret said she thought it would be all right, and Pamela promised to come and see her before she left for America, to make sure she was. So the die was cast.

Mr Green confirmed that he would bring Margaret at the weekend. Saturday was to be the day she moved. Pamela shook hands with Mrs Hall before they all departed.

During the next few days she once more reluctantly packed her things. Her suitcase was not big enough for all of them. Pamela had bought her a lot of clothes. Another suitcase was found up in the loft, as well as a bag to put her books and dolly in.

On Friday she had to say farewell to her school teacher Miss Hughes, and to the friends she had made and played with. She had no time to say goodbye to the Reverend Hewitt.

On Friday evening Pamela cooked Margaret's favourite dinner of fish and chips, then sat down together on the sofa and talked for hours. Pamela telling her how she had to pack up all her mother's things, and give some away, as well as packing her own trunks ready to go on a big ship to America. She herself hated the idea of leaving so many friends and people she knew, but added she felt it was for the best; she loved James and felt she would soon be part of his family. She gave Margaret a photograph she had taken of the child in the back garden some weeks before.

'This will remind you of me; do you remember we had just come back from town, and I had enough money to buy a film for the camera?' Margaret smiled, yes she remembered what a lovely day it had been. They had toured the shops looking for a small present for Mrs Perie as it was coming up to her birthday. Pamela had found she had a small amount of money left over, and in a rash moment had purchased the film. They looked through other photographs, remembering different people, and discovering people she didn't know at all. Mrs Perie had been a beautiful woman when she was young, and so smartly dressed. How she missed her.

They stayed up late, and at 10 o'clock Margaret eventually went up to bed for the last time in this lovely house. Pamela tucked her in and wished her goodnight. But sleep would not come, and she tossed and turned for a long time, before finally falling into an exhausted sleep.

*

When Saturday dawned, everything was packed. She went downstairs and clung to Pamela. Tears flowed down her cheeks. Oh, she was going to miss Pamela. Why did she have to leave? She had been happy here.

She helped Pamela pack some of her things into a trunk. Some of the nice books and ornaments into one, and clothes into another. They had lunch together, but Margaret didn't feel very hungry, and every bite tasted like cardboard.

Mr Green arrived at 3 o'clock, and put her cases and bags into the little black car, and shortly she was once more clambering into the front seat. Pamela gave her one last cuddle, then stood at the gate and waved until the car was out of sight. She had once again promised to come and see her before she sailed to America.

Mr Green drove the car along the High Street, and stopped outside a little shop. He got out of the car, went into the shop, and bought her an ice cream cornet. 'There you are Margaret, I'm sure you like ice cream.'

She did, ooh, what a treat. 'Thank you Mr Green,' she said. Pamela occasionally bought her an ice cream. She licked at it as the car continued towards Maple Avenue.

Mr Green took Margaret up to the front door, and they were once more invited in by Mrs Hall. He had carried both her suitcases, and she had carried the bag containing her doll Jane. They entered the hallway, and Margaret began to realise how dingy everything looked. She hadn't noticed before how brown the walls were, and the curtains were faded. The carpet, also brown, was threadbare in places. Mrs Hall still had her pinny on.

Mr Green only stayed a short while, telling Mrs Hall he would return in a few days, to give Margaret time to settle, and to see how she was.

Mrs Hall told her to take her things upstairs. She picked up one of the suitcases, and spent some time emptying some of her things into the chest of drawers Mrs Hall had indicated. She put Jane on the unused bed.

Just before tea Betty arrived, so for the first time she saw the girl she was to share a bedroom with. She found she was very slim, and had curly blonde hair. She giggled quite a lot while she introduced herself, and Margaret decided she would like living with Betty.

Betty helped her take up the second suitcase, which was much heavier, and they struggled up the stairs with it. More drawers were filled. Betty admired some of the clothes that Pamela had bought, especially the plum coloured dress with the smocking on the front, that she mainly kept for going to church.

'Oh, it is nice to have you here Margaret,' Betty retorted, 'we can have such good fun. I have been here for a long time on my own, and Mrs Hall, Aunty Ann, is not a lot of fun.' She went on to tell Margaret, 'Aunty Ann is my real aunt. I have lived all my life in London with my mother and father, and when the war started they sent me here to my aunt's.' Betty went on to say, 'Aunty Ann is very lazy, and expects me to do a lot of chores round the house, and run errands, while she sits in her favourite armchair. She smokes a lot of cigarettes, and likes a glass of stout in the evenings, if she can afford it. But she's all right, you'll see.'

Margaret wasn't so sure, her days with Mr and Mrs Jones came to her mind, and all the chores she had been expected to do.

Betty, realising she had painted a rather desolate picture about life at Maple Avenue, suddenly said, 'You'll be all right, Aunty Ann won't expect you to do much, she will get paid for looking after you, it's probably because I'm family.'

The girls chatted for quite a while upstairs on their own. Margaret told Betty that she had not wanted to come. She had liked it where she had been staying with Mrs Perie, but that the lovely lady had died, and now Pamela, her daughter, was going off to America on a big ship.

Betty felt sorry for the girl and said, 'You can have the bed by the door if you like,' she offered. 'It's the most comfortable, I have been using it, but you can have it.'

Margaret thanked her, and moved Jane onto the other bed.

Betty went on to tell Margaret about the school she would be going to. 'It's a long way,' she told her, 'and you will have to walk.' She went on 'It's not a bad school, but if you are late in the morning you get the cane. So you'll have to get up fairly early.'

Goodness, thought Margaret. *I will have to set out early and be sure I get there on time.* The thought of the cane worried her.

She told Betty all about her last school, and that she had been in the choir and loved singing *Jerusalem* and the *Welsh National Anthem,* now that she knew it. Betty however, did not seem much impressed. Betty seemed quite like Jane Jones, but a little younger. She was in fact a year older than Margaret. Both girls were quite excited when they went downstairs. It was nice that she had Betty to talk to, just as

Pamela had told her, and she would surely become a good friend.

Mrs Hall had already laid the table, but Betty told her that usually she had to do that as well as many other things. Mrs Hall was a widow and had few interests. Margaret soon saw that what Betty had said about her aunt was true. A cigarette was hanging out of the corner of Mrs Hall's mouth. All the time she was doing things the cigarette remained there, and Margaret was fascinated that it never fell out when she was talking, and also about how long the ash remained getting longer without dropping onto the carpet.

Tea consisted of bread and jam, and some rock cakes Mrs Hall had made herself; and rocks they were. Margaret missed the nice dinner she was used to eating at about 6 o'clock each day. Still, she wasn't hungry now. She had eaten some tea, and after playing a game of ludo with Betty she went off to bed.

Neither Mrs Hall nor Betty went to church on Sundays, and the day dragged. The only outstanding thing that happened was that Betty took her for a walk around the area, so that she knew where she was. Mrs Hall sat and smoked one cigarette after another, while listening to the wireless. Betty had been sent to fetch a newspaper from the shop for her, and she sat reading the paper from cover to cover, commenting on what was happening in the war. There appeared to be no let up in the Battle of Britain. The air force were sending planes up every day, trying to outwit the Germans.

*

Margaret was a little apprehensive on Monday morning. They got up and dressed, and after breakfast of cornflakes, bread and Marmite, Betty took Margaret to Acton Park

School. Gosh, it was a long way. They walked through the estate where the house was, down an alley that led to a pathway, and across a field, before climbing over a stile gate and entering the road which led up to the school. The wind had been blowing and she felt a mess by the time they arrived.

Betty took her to the school office, and told the lady there that Margaret was starting school that day. She also told her that she had come to live with her Aunty, but really was from London. 'Oh, you mean she is an evacuee, Betty?' the woman said. She looked at Margaret and said, 'You had better wait here until it is decided where you are to go.'

She sat on a bench in the corridor, and watched all the children file past, going to their classrooms. There were a few children darting about with school registers in their hands. It was a big school, much bigger than the one she had just left. It was also much more modern, and the ceilings were lower.

At least she knew some Welsh, even though she didn't know any of the other children except Betty. Before leaving her, Betty had said she would see her in the playground at break time, so she didn't feel all alone.

Eventually she was taken to a classroom by the lady in the school office. Class C. She took an instant dislike to the teacher, she was not like Miss Hughes at her other school. Nevertheless, she soon settled into the class she was put in, and within a few days was fairly accepted by the other children. Mrs Porter, her new teacher, who Margaret thought was a dragon, seemed to mellow when she discovered that the child was quite good at her school work, and that she was a nice quiet girl, who did not appear to cause any trouble.

On that first day she was not looking forward to the long walk home, and she dreaded the thought that she had to walk so far to school every day. But providing it was dry it would not be too bad. Unfortunately, Margaret had discovered that living in North Wales you had to expect rain and cold winds most of the time, and in winter lots of snow. The worst times were when it poured with rain, when she would be wet through, and if she arrived at school wet in the mornings, she had to remain so for the rest of the day.

By Thursday of that week she felt tired out. Almost straight after tea each day she went upstairs to their bedroom, and before she knew it she was fast asleep. She had never felt so tired. Betty seemed so used to it, and often on the walk home from school left Margaret lagging behind.

Friday dawned. It was a fine day, and feeling quite refreshed from her long sleep the night before, she skipped of to school with Betty. She had already started to make a few friends, and she quite liked the school, it was Mrs Porter she was wary of.

Mrs Hall was quite pleasant to her, although she wasn't nice and friendly like Pamela had been, nor did she sit and talk with her. Once home from school there was really only Betty. However, Betty had a friend who lived down the Avenue, who soon showed she was not too happy to have Margaret tag along all the time. She often tried to persuade Betty for them to go off together on their own.

But all in all things were not too bad, nowhere near as bad as when she had lived with the Jones' family.

*

That Friday afternoon she was pleasantly surprised to see Mr Green's car outside the house on her return from school. She dashed indoors, looking most dishevelled. On seeing her he rose from his seat, 'Hello Margaret, I was just telling

Mrs Hall, I was in the area and thought I would pop in and see how things were going.'

'Hello Mr Green,' she replied, 'it is nice to see you.' She went on, 'I thought Pamela might be with you.'

'I am afraid not my dear, I am afraid I haven't spoken to her this week, I might drop by soon.' He smiled at her. 'How is your new school?' he enquired.

Margaret felt very disappointed that Pamela had not come with him, it had seemed an age since she had seen her, even though it had only been a week. How she missed her.

'It felt strange at first, but I quite like it, although I miss Miss Hughes, and some of my friends, but I now have a friend called Judy,' she told him.

'Splendid, I am pleased to hear it.' Once more he smiled at her. 'You have Betty as well, don't you?'

'Yes,' she replied, 'I quite like Betty.'

'Well, that's fine.' He turned to Mrs Hall. 'Thank you for your kind hospitality, I'll see myself out.'

The next minute he was gone.

Margaret went upstairs. She threw her things down on the bed and changed into one of her older dresses. It was Friday, so she could stay in bed a little longer tomorrow, no need to get up so early, there was no school.

Goodness, she had forgotten to tell Mr Green how far she had to walk to school. *Oh well,* she thought, *I'll tell him when he comes next time.* After all, she was sure he would bring Pamela to see her before she left for America.

While they were having tea that day, Mrs Hall told her that the following morning she would be going shopping, and would set off at half past eight. Betty said she would be going to her friend's house. 'Oh well Margaret, you can come with me, as soon as we have cleared breakfast.'

Oh no, she thought, *I had expected to lie in bed a little longer tomorrow,* but there was nothing for it, she would have to go.

* * *

Chapter 8

Margaret helped Mrs Hall carry home the shopping the following morning from the local shop. The two bags she carried were very heavy. One was full of potatoes and carrots, and the other had various tins of things. Mrs Hall seemed to know a lot of people and kept stopping to talk to lots of ladies about her own age. One or two of them looked down at Margaret, and Mrs Hall was quick to tell them that she had taken in one of the evacuees, seeing it as her bit towards the war effort. Margaret found it most embarrassing, and also wished she would hurry up because of the heavy bags.

On their return to the house, she went upstairs and played with her dolly Jane, and did some drawing. Betty did not come back until late afternoon, just in time to lay the table for tea. She never said where she had been, nor did Mrs Hall ask her.

Sunday was just a repeat of Saturday. Nothing particular to do. Betty once more went to her friend's house, and did not ask Margaret to accompany her. So Margaret spent most of the day up in their bedroom.

She had become used to taking up a jug of water to wash with in the mornings. She missed the little bathroom at Victoria Road; still, it was better than having to go down to the scullery with all the other children at the Jones's house.

She missed going to Church, and all the nice hymns which were sung. She decided to go down and ask Mrs Hall if she could go to the local church the following Sunday.

Mrs Hall was in her favourite chair, puffing away at a cigarette.

'Mrs Hall, may I go to Church next Sunday? I miss going,' she asked. The woman looked at Margaret.

'I'm afraid I don't believe in church,' she replied. 'It is a long walk, so you can't go on your own.' She went on, 'Ask Betty if she will go with you,' she was turning her attention back to the book she was reading. 'Now run along, and don't bother me, there's a good girl.'

There was nothing for it, she had been dismissed. She went back upstairs. Mrs Hall didn't like the girls remaining in the sitting room. She sat on her bed, there was nothing to do, and no one to talk to. She felt so lonely.

Betty again returned for tea, and dutifully laid the table. Margaret took the opportunity to ask Betty about going with her to Church on Sundays, but when she mentioned this, Betty looked at her in horror, and shook her head.

'No, Sunday is a fun day when I go out with my friends,' she said to Margaret.

'But we could all go,' Margaret persisted, but Betty was adamant.

When they both went upstairs, having cleared away the tea things, both girls were silent. Margaret kept looking at Betty. She had thought they would be good friends, but Betty preferred to go out all the time, and where did she really go?

A little while later, Mrs Hall called the girls downstairs. 'As there are two of you now, I have decided that you can share the work in the house between you. Betty, you can continue to clean the lavvy and wash up. Margaret is quite old enough to lay the table and run errands.'

Margaret thought *Well, I can lay the table*, she didn't mind that too much, *after all, it would be something to do.* She wasn't sure what "errands" meant, but it didn't sound too bad.

On the Monday she went to school as usual, and came home and laid the table for tea. It was not until Tuesday morning that she found out what "errands" meant.

She had just finished her breakfast, with enough time to spare to put her shoes and coat on, when Mrs Hall came into the kitchen and said to Margaret, 'I need some marmalade from the shop for my breakfast, I have run out.' Margaret wasn't sure she was hearing right. The shop was two roads away. There wasn't time.

'Please Mrs Hall, I have to go to school now, or I'll be late,' she cried.

'Don't answer me back young lady, I need some marmalade,' she went on, 'it won't take you long to run there and back.'

Mrs Hall went out of the kitchen saying over her shoulder, 'You can see Mrs Morgan in the shop, and she will put it on the slate until the weekend.'

Margaret stared at her retreating figure, Mrs Hall turned and said, 'Go on, hurry up or you'll be late for school.'

Margaret flew out of the house, putting her coat on as she went down the garden path. She ran like fury out of the Avenue down Chestnut Avenue, and on to the main road. She panted hard as she neared the shop; then dashed inside. Mrs Morgan was serving another lady.

'Oh, hello Margaret, I won't be a minute love,' she said. Margaret felt very impatient, especially as the two women were chatting about local events.

'And how is young Jamie doing at football Mrs Robinson?' she asked the customer.

'Oh, thanks for asking, Mrs Morgan, he is doing very well.'

At last the customer left, and it was her turn.

'I want a jar of marmalade for Mrs Hall please, and can you put it on the slate for her?' she asked.

'Certainly dear, which sort of marmalade does she usually have?' she asked the child.

'Oh, I don't know,' Margaret felt stupid, she hadn't thought to ask. She had been in such a hurry.

The kindly lady in the shop said, 'Well, I'll give you this Robertson's one, that should be all right, mind you, don't drop it will you dear.'

'I won't,' Margaret replied, as she grabbed the jar, and ran out of the shop, running as fast as her legs could go, back to the house.

Mrs Hall was talking over the fence to the next-door neighbour Mrs Thomas; her usual cigarette drooping from her mouth. Margaret dashed indoors and put the marmalade on the table, grabbed her school bag, and was out of the door.

She ran and ran over the field pathways to school. She could hear the school bell ringing from some way off. Oh, goodness, she was going to be late. She tried to run faster, but as she neared the school she had to slow down, she had a stitch in her side.

She ran across the playground, there was no one in sight, everyone had gone in. She went through the main door and into the cloakroom to hang her coat up.

Mr Johns, the headmaster, was standing there.

'And where have you been until now, young lady?' he asked.

'Oh, I had to run an errand, Mr Johns, I am sorry for being late.'

'You know you have to be at school for 9 o'clock, it is now 9.15 am,' he glared at her. 'I suggest you go and wait outside my office,' he told her.

Margaret felt her knees shake, her stomach felt so nervous. *Oh, goodness what now?* She went along the corridor and waited outside Mr Johns' office, and stood there for quite some time. She was missing her favourite lesson, English.

Some while later, Mr Johns appeared, and told Margaret to follow him into his office.

She stood very still.

'As this is your first time being late, I have decided that you will stay after school and write twenty lines. Come back here at 4 o'clock.' She was dismissed.

Unbeknown to her, Mr Johns had spoken to her teacher, who had said she was usually punctual, and was a hard worker in class. Mr Johns had therefore decided not to cane the child, he felt rather sorry for her, learning that she had only recently come to live in the area, and was an evacuee. So he had decided to give her a few lines instead.

Margaret went off to her classroom. *Oh dea*r, she thought, *what would Mrs Hall say if she was late home, and didn't lay the table for tea?*

All day she couldn't concentrate, and she started day dreaming, only to be told off by Mrs Porter, her teacher. It seemed she could do nothing right.

At 4 o'clock she sat in the corridor, being jeered at by some of the children poking fun at her. Everyone seemed to know she had to stay in. At ten past four, Mr Johns took Margaret into a classroom and wrote on the blackboard, "I must not be late for school".

'I want you to write that twenty times and bring it to me when you have finished, do you understand?'

'Yes, Mr Johns, she replied.

It shouldn't take long, and she could run all the way to the house. At 4.30pm she had finished, and dutifully went back to Mr Johns' office and knocked at the door. It was slightly ajar, and it soon became obvious that he wasn't there. She could see into his office and it was empty. *Oh, where can he be?* she thought worriedly.

There was nothing for it, she would have to wait until he came. Another ten minutes went by, it seemed like an hour as Margaret became increasingly anxious all the time. Eventually, he came down the corridor, went past her, and beckoned her into his office.

He took the piece of paper that she handed him, grunted, and then said, 'You have been let off lightly this time. Make sure you are not late again, or you will get the cane.' Margaret promised she would be on time in future.

He bid her good afternoon.

Margaret ran to the cloakroom to collect her coat, and ran as hard as she could all the way home to Maple Avenue.

As she opened the back door and entered, Mrs Hall turned round from the sink and said, 'And where have you been until now? You should have been home by half past four, and it is now ten past five.'

'I am sorry Mrs Hall, I had to stay in because I was late for school this morning, as I had to go to the shop for you,' she replied. She could feel herself shaking.

'Which reminds me young lady, you brought the wrong marmalade, I like chunky, kindly remember that in future,' she chided.

'Yes Mrs Hall, I'll try.'

'Go and change and wash your hands, and brush your hair, you are in an untidy state.'

'Yes Mrs Hall.'

She ran upstairs. Goodness, she had never been told off so much in a day, and all for a jar of marmalade. No, she didn't like doing errands.

Tea was late that day, and she was constantly reminded by Mrs Hall of her wrongdoings.

'You had better get up earlier each morning in case I need something from the shop, then you won't be late for school,' she told Margaret.

This was easier said than done.

Margaret did not mind going to the shop, or taking messages to other people, or posting letters, if it was after school, which it quite often was. Many times she went to the shop to get cigarettes for Mrs Hall. "Twenty Woodbines" was the usual order. Mrs Morgan at the shop quite often reached for the cigarettes as soon as she saw Margaret, even if she wasn't going for any. Although nine out of ten times she was.

She tried to get up a little earlier, and occasionally when she had to go to the shop in the morning before school she managed to just get to school before registration.

However, some two weeks later, she overslept a little, and Betty took her time using the washbasin. Margaret went downstairs to have her breakfast, and learnt to her horror that Mrs Hall needed some groceries. 'We are out of milk and bread,' she said, 'as well as that I only have two fags left. Nip down to the shop quickly Margaret.'

Ice cold fear gripped Margaret's heart. No matter how fast she ran she was going to be late.

When she arrived at the school, once more no one was in sight. She crept into the cloakroom, and was just hanging up her coat when she was pounced on by a prefect. He hauled her off to the front corridor to join three other children, all lined up. Mr Johns came out of his office carrying a cane in his hand. He asked each child why they were late for school. Then he asked them to raise their left hands. Each child received a crack of the stick across the palm. Margaret was beside herself. Oh the indignity. Oh the pain. There was a long red mark across the palm of her hand. Never had anyone struck her like this. She stood bemused, and although she felt like crying, she bit hard on her lip to stop herself. It was all Mrs Hall's fault, and also Betty's for delaying her this morning. She had risen early enough, with time to spare to go to the shop as well.

'Off you all go back to your classes, and let me remind you not to be late again,' Mr Johns retorted.

He had been surprised to see Margaret in the line up, she obviously hadn't heeded his words from the last time, and he had been reasonably fair with her. Well, perhaps the cane would be an added incentive to make sure she wasn't late again. He had obviously been too soft with her.

Margaret ran into the cloakroom, and at last she let the tears flow. She ran her sore hand under the cold tap. It just wasn't fair. She had done her best, no one understood.

Margaret was to join the line up on many occasions after that. The thought of the cane preoccupied her mind both in school and at home.

As well as the cane at school, Mrs Hall also kept a cane in the corner of the sitting room. Margaret had never seen her use it or refer to it.

It had been some weeks before Margaret had even been aware of it. One day she was upstairs with Betty when Mrs Hall came raging upstairs and said to Betty, 'Have you been in my purse again? I have some money missing.' Margaret knew she herself hadn't touched it; even so her heart froze on seeing the rage Mrs Hall was in.

'Not me,' replied Betty.

Mrs Hall continued to question Betty, and eventually told Betty to go downstairs. Betty went, followed by Mrs Hall. Margaret crept along the landing to find out what was going on. There were raised voices downstairs.

Mrs Hall spat at Betty, 'I knew you had taken it, you thieving little devil.'

'I'm sorry,' she heard Betty reply, 'I won't do it again.'

But the next instant Mrs Hall had the cane in her hand and was hitting Betty with it. Betty shrieked out loud. She started crying. Mrs Hall then said, 'Get up to your room.'

Mrs Hall saw Margaret looking over the balustrade. 'You needn't fret,' she said, 'I won't hit you with it unless you are really naughty.' She went on, 'I want Betty to grow up to be a decent girl. She has to learn.'

Margaret went back into the bedroom and stared at Betty.

'Goodness, your aunt is horrible isn't she?' she said to her friend.

Betty said, 'I hate her, she is a cruel woman, but if I tell my mother she will hit me as well, so I can't win.'

Betty had a few nasty red wheals on her arm and leg. Margaret felt so sorry for her. Betty said, 'I only took two shillings, I know my parents send Aunty Ann some money for me, but I never get it, so I took it.'

Margaret was soon to learn that Betty was often in trouble from time to time, because she took things. Sometimes she took things from school, and sometimes from other people's houses, and sometimes from Mrs Hall. The canings never stopped her stealing. Margaret was later to realise what an unhappy, insecure child Betty was.

*

As April turned into May, and then June, things got a little better. The weather had improved, and she arrived at school mostly dry, as there was less rain.

The light mornings woke her early and she could get any errands done, and still get to school on time, though some mornings she only just beat the bell.

Mr Green did not make any further house visits for some while. She never heard again from Pamela Perie, who had promised to come and see her before she sailed for America. Each day since she came to live with Mrs Hall she had hoped against hope for Pamela to come and see her, and even for her to come and say she had changed her mind, that she could go back to live at Victoria Road. How she missed her life there.

However, she did receive occasional letters from her mother. She dearly wanted to hear from John.

Surely it could not be long now before she went home. Mr Green had intimated to her on his last visit that the war seemed likely to end soon. Only yesterday the newscaster on the little wireless had said that the allies had invaded Normandy. Mrs Hall had become quite excited and said, 'That will show those Nazis they can't do what they like.' The newscaster went on to say the Red Army was gathering itself for an attack on the Eastern Front. It would be a true demonstration of power. *Surely the war was coming to an end,* she thought.

It was some two weeks later on the 22nd June 1944 that one of the newscasters advised that the Red Army had attacked, and the offensive had wiped out German Forces around Minsk. Margaret had taken to listening carefully to the wireless on a daily basis, and started to realise things were hotting up.

*

The summer wore on and no word came from Mr Green. Margaret thought she'd heard that the war had ended some weeks ago and had been so certain that she would be returning to London. Perhaps her mother didn't want her back. At school the other evacuee children were all expectant that they would be returning home, but no word came.

The school summer holidays loomed large, and Margaret wondered whatever she would find to do for so many weeks. There was no money to go on a holiday to the seaside, even though she knew that some of the children from school were going to Llandudno.

There was no way that Margaret wanted to be in the house all day and every day, so she went to see Mrs Morgan at the local shop.

'Hello Margaret, what would Mrs Hall like today?' she enquired.

'Nothing today Mrs Morgan, I was just wondering if there was anything I could do for you during the school holidays?'

'You mean do some work? Well, I often need someone to help me but you are such a little thing, I would have to think what you could do. If Mrs Hall has no objection I suppose you could tidy up for me, and fill up some of the shelves, and you could possibly make up the orders. I tell you what Margaret, I'll have a think about it, while you talk to Mrs Hall.'

Later that day, Margaret tentatively sought out the good lady. She listened to what the child said, without making any comment. Eventually she said, 'I don't mind if you work there for a few hours each day, so long as you do your chores here.'

Margaret couldn't believe her luck, and the following day she returned to see Mrs Morgan.

She said, 'I would be delighted to have some help Margaret, perhaps you could start tomorrow, and help me packet the tea and sugar. If you work each morning I'll find some extra rations for you.'

Gosh, that would please Mrs Hall, Margaret thought.

The little job helped her pass the holiday and Mrs Hall was delighted with the little extras that Margaret brought home.

In September just before school started again Betty's mother and father arrived for a visit, and took her out to purchase some clothing. They had saved some clothing coupons to enable them to do this. Betty had wanted a best dress like Margaret's, but she was to be disappointed. Her parents bought her "sensible clothes" ready for the winter. Her parents were nice, but they took no notice of Margaret, and Betty was the centre of attention for just a few days. Mrs Hall made a special tea for Betty's birthday, but the girl had looked most disappointed when she opened her present, a pair of bed socks. There were no hot water bottles in this house, and Margaret rather envied her the nice warm woolly socks.

'Aunty Ann has made some gingerbread men,' Betty told her. They were upstairs, where they had been sent, while the grown-ups were busy talking downstairs.

'Has she really?' Margaret's eyes beamed. The last time she had eaten any was when Mrs Perie had made them for her, a real luxury considering the shortages of ingredients to make them. But the extra sugar she had brought home from the shop had helped.

Mrs Hall never appeared to mention to Betty's parents how naughty their daughter was from time to time, and Betty never mentioned the canings either.

Betty waved a fond farewell to her parents, and promptly went out down the road to her friend's house, leaving Margaret once more on her own.

Margaret hoped that her mother was going to come to visit her for her own birthday, which was only a few short weeks away in October. After all, she had come the year before. She wrote to her mother, telling her she missed her, and asking if she could come to Wales for her birthday.

Alas, no! She learned in a letter she received that there was no money for her to come to North Wales. The letter worried her a great deal. She learned two things besides that her mother was not coming to visit.

Firstly, the family had moved from Upminster in Essex, and were now living in Richmond in Surrey. *Goodness,* she thought, *where on earth is Richmond?* Secondly, her mother told her that John had left college and was now working.

Her mother's letters gave very little information, but she loved to receive them. She always wrote back furiously, straight away.

Over the last few months she had told her mother all about her school, but never worried her about the difficulties she had to cope with living with Mrs Hall. She thought her mother had enough to cope with. She felt things were not too bad, but she did want to go home. While she had lived with Mr Perie her need to go home had lessened, but now she wanted to leave Wales so passionately.

Her birthday came and went, there was no birthday tea, nothing special. Betty gave her a sachet of lavender in a little bag she had made, to put with her clothes. Mrs Hall, ever practical, had given her some ribbon for her hair. Plain white. She felt very deflated, thinking of the lovely things Pamela and Mrs Perie had given her. And no visit from her mother. No card came either.

The war went on, the RAF was carrying out raids over Germany, and last week they had raided Duisburg. Just before her birthday the newscaster had stated that Rommel had committed suicide. Every country appeared to be attacking the Germans. Surely the Germans would surrender soon. Troops had stormed the Auschwitz camps and the gassing had come to an end. The thought of those poor people made Margaret cringe at the cruelty being meted out. When she went to Church she used to pray for the poor Jews.

Christmas loomed large on the calendar. Mrs Perie had taught her to sew, and as she had no money as such, she started making small things for both Mrs Hall and Betty for

Christmas presents. For Betty she made a hair band from ribbons, and for Mrs Hall she knitted a pot holder.

They started preparing for the big day. Mrs Hall had been promised a goose. Some things had been kept and stored over the last few weeks. They made paper chains to put up, so that the house looked nice and decorated. The little tree was adorned with coloured pieces of paper, and all the presents were placed underneath.

Mrs Hall was in a very good mood, and made pastry tarts, and a jelly for tea. The neighbours from next door came in and brought a few plates of food with them. Everyone appeared to enjoy themselves. Mrs Hall bought her a book, because she knew Margaret liked reading, and Betty bought her some sweets from her pocket money, which also cost her some of her precious sweet ration. Both girls only had a penny a week pocket money, so considerable personal sacrifice would have been made.

She decided that Christmas had been most enjoyable and wished the atmosphere would continue. That night when the neighbours finally went home she sat up in bed and talked with Betty. 'I never realised that your Aunty Ann could be so nice,' she said.

Betty, who was busy brushing her hair with the hairbrush Mrs Hall had given her for Christmas, turned round and smiled at her. 'She's not a bad old stick, I just resent having to stay here for so long. When I was told by my mother that I would be going to stay with Aunty Ann for a short while I thought she had meant just a few weeks at most. I suppose it isn't Aunty Ann's fault she has got lumbered with me for so long either.' She went on, 'When my mother came recently she felt it would not be long before the Germans were defeated, then perhaps we could go home.'

Margaret nodded. *If only . . .*

It had been the first time that she had seen Mrs Hall drunk, certainly very merry. Both she and the lady next door had been tippling some port. Betty had brought the bottle upstairs with her. There was a little drop in the bottom, which they both shared. It tasted nice and made you feel funny.

*

The New Year dawned – 1945. Was she never going home?

The weather was very cold, and the roads were covered in snow and ice. Margaret hated the cold. There was no heating upstairs and she missed the stone hot water bottle that Pamela used to put in her bed. She envied the bed socks that Betty's parents had bought her for her birthday. She would wrap an old cardigan round her feet to try to keep them warm.

She had not heard from her mother for some while. The letters had stopped coming before her birthday in October. Did her mother not love her any more? Did her mother ever think about her? She must do sometimes.

The snow lay very deep during January and February. Getting to school had become difficult. The pathway across the fields was continually blocked with snow. The journey took twice as long. Margaret now had the extra task of going out and collecting wood for the fire, and bringing in the coal. Coal often consisted of peat blocks. The house was never very warm. The only warm place was in the armchair where Mrs Hall sat most of the time.

In February a surprise visit from Mr Green cheered her. On returning from school one afternoon she saw that his car was parked outside the house. She ran indoors, and straight away he stood up and greeted her.

'Why hello Margaret, how are you my dear?' he asked.

'I'm fine,' she smiled at him. She had missed seeing him. She sat down opposite Mrs Hall, who had not moved out of her chair.

Mr Green told her it should not be long before the war was over; Mr Churchill had made a speech in the House of Commons intimating such. Oh good, she would be going home.

* * *

Chapter 9

Margaret was excited, there seemed a possibility that she was going home. Mr Green had brought some treats for the two girls. When Betty arrived they shared the barley sticks, and some rock that he had brought from Rhyl. He told them that he had been visiting the factory that made the rock, and the proprietor had offered him a variety of the firm's produce for the evacuee children. The children were not to know that the produce was imperfect. It did taste good though.

Mr Green stayed for tea that day, and the girls enjoyed being spoilt by Mrs Hall, who was obviously trying to impress Mr Green. Mrs Hall laid the table, and had some nice cakes with icing on them for tea. They had meat paste in their sandwiches instead of jam.

Mr Green told them stories about other children, and about his own wife and family. Margaret had never realised he had a family of his own.

He told them he had three children. His eldest son was in the Army, and currently stationed near Dover. He had heard from Ernest recently, and feared he may have to go to France shortly, with his battalion. Then there was Samantha, who was fifteen years old, and had left school last year. She worked in a local draper's shop. And lastly there was Johnny, who was eleven. He was at the Grammar School, but he had to travel to Bangor, and during term time he stayed with Mr Green's sister Rose, who lived in Bangor. So he saw little of his children.

All too soon Mr Green had to go. The girls were not too surprised to learn that they were washing up the tea things, and Mrs Hall immediately retired to her chair by the fire, and lit a cigarette.

During March, Margaret persuaded Mrs Hall to let her go to the Church further along Rhosnesni Lane on her own. She had been to church quite a few times, but only when Mrs Hughes from two doors down went, which wasn't as often as she would have liked to go. Mrs Hall finally agreed, as she didn't have to cross a main road. So she went to the 11 o'clock service each Sunday morning. Betty had no interest in going, choosing to go out with her friends. Margaret found that her friend Judy from school went to the same church with her family, and she looked forward to this enjoyable time. She loved the hymns, and the vicar was very nice, and told nice stories to the congregation. The prayers were always about the war, and were asking God that people came back safe, or that the men folk were kept safe down the mines. Sons, daughters and husbands, Margaret asked only for the war to end.

Only that week she had finally received a letter from her mother. She learnt that her brother William had a girlfriend called Ellen, whose parents lived in Rhyl, and her mother had intimated that William might come and see her in Wrexham when he was next on leave. She didn't know much about her eldest brother. He was so much older than her, and when she had been at home he was always away. But she thought it would be nice to see him. Alas, he never came.

Margaret was made a member of the choir at school, and her music teacher also played the organ at St Clements' Church. Margaret got on well with Miss Brown, so it wasn't long before she was accepted into the choir at the church. This meant she was out of the house for much longer periods, and Sundays became her favourite day. She could talk to her friend Judy, enjoy the service, and sing in the choir. She also had to attend choir practice on Wednesday evenings after tea.

After the school holiday for Easter, Margaret went to school one morning, and as she approached the school gate she noticed there were two teachers standing by the entrance. She was told, along with other children, that there would be no school that day as the trees that were right next to the classrooms were infested with bees.

As she retraced her steps she could see in the distance men with funny hats covered in netting, walking about in the trees. Betty, who usually went to school with her friend Penny from down the road, caught up with her.

'Isn't it great,' she said, 'no school today.'

'It means a day at the house though,' Margaret replied.

'How about not going to the house, Aunty Ann won't know we are not safely at school will she?' she said to her.

Margaret wasn't so sure. She didn't like the idea of having to be cooped up in the house all day either, but felt she should go and tell Mrs Hall there was not any school that day.

'I think we should go home first,' she said to Betty.

'If we go home, she'll find us something to do,' Betty chided. 'I'm not going, please yourself. Also, it will look funny if you go home, and I don't turn up. Oh, come on Margaret, don't be a spoil sport.'

Penny said, 'It will be fun, oh come on, be a sport.'

Margaret decided they were right. They skipped down the rest of the pathway, and turned down Chestnut Avenue, and walked along Oak Drive. They passed Mrs Morgan's little shop, all giggling together. They were later to regret this. Margaret felt happy to be included with Betty and Penny. They had always excluded her before.

Unbeknown to them, later that morning, Mrs Hall went down the road to get some egg powder from the shop.

'Oh, hello, Mrs Hall,' said Mrs Morgan. 'I'll get you some egg powder from out the back, I don't keep it on display, it's so hard to come by.' She returned immediately with a little brown paper bag.

'Where were the girls going this morning?' she asked.

'Going?' answered Mrs Hall,' they both went off to school at the usual time, or I would have sent Margaret to get this.'

'Well, I could have sworn it was both of them that passed here about an hour ago, with Penny Simpson,' she retorted. Three girls passed here, making a lot of noise, giggling.'

Mrs Hall thought for a moment, then said, 'Do you think they were playing truant?'

Mrs Morgan said, 'They could be of course, but it is unlike Margaret to do something like that. As far as Betty is concerned, and that Penny Simpson, I wouldn't put it past them.'

Mrs Hall returned home. All day she thought about it. She smoked heavily, until half past four when the two girls returned home. They had spent some of the day in town. They were very hungry as they had not had any dinner at school. Meals at school were horrible, but at least they stopped you from feeling hungry. They had met up with two other children from their school, and all five had walked up from town and walked into Acton Park to play on the swings and slide. One boy had made a paper boat and had tried to sail it on the lake. Some of them had taken off their socks and shoes, and paddled at the edge of the lake. The day had flown.

The two children who had joined them earlier had already been home, but as their parents had been out at work they had found themselves at a loose end. All five had returned to their house with them and ransacked the cupboard for something to eat. There was little to have, just a few biscuits and some milk.

Betty and Margaret arrived home and went in the back door as usual. Mrs Hall told the girls to come into the parlour. She did not look very pleased with them. The two girls were also feeling very guilty. Mrs Hall couldn't possibly know where they had been. They had come in at the right time as though they were coming home from school.

'Tell me no lies, where have you two been today?' she demanded. Betty and Margaret looked at each other. Goodness, what could they say?

Mrs Hall went on, 'I know you haven't been to school, you were seen with that Penny Simpson going towards the High Street.'

Margaret started to cry. She knew she should never have gone. Betty was always getting her into trouble. Betty was a nice girl, but she was always in trouble.

'Well, answer me,' Mrs Hall shouted.

Betty spoke up, 'There was no school today, so we went for a walk.'

'You went for a walk without telling me?' Mrs Hall's voice soared as she glared at the two girls. 'Why was there no school?' Before they could answer she said, 'I don't believe you, I think you have been playing truant, you have, haven't you?'

Both girls started to say 'No,' but in an instant Mrs Hall turned and reached for the cane in the corner. 'Bend over, both of you,' she roared, I'll teach you to play truant.'

As the girls obeyed and bent over, the cane whacked across the backs of their thighs. Oh, the pain! They discovered two red wheals across the backs of their legs after they had been sent upstairs. 'You'll both go without any tea,' Mrs Hall declared.

Both girls cried. Margaret wanted to run away. Even the cane at school had never hurt this much. Mrs Hall was horrible. She had not given them a chance to explain, and they were so hungry.

It was some two days later that Mrs Hall found out that the girls had been telling the truth, that they had not been playing truant, and that all the children had been sent home from school Nevertheless, she was cross with them for not having come home straight away. She, herself, had had to walk to the shop, when one of them could have gone.

However, she was a little kinder to them, and on the Saturday she was feeling she ought to make it up to them for having caned them. She took them into town and bought them each a penny ice cream. This was just a wafer, with a little bit of ice cream on one corner, but a rare treat.

Margaret hated Mrs Hall. She now understood why Betty disliked her so. Not only was she fond of using the cane, but she was also unfair and unfeeling.

*

In May 1945 Margaret couldn't believe what she heard on the wireless. It crackled a lot, and you had to listen hard, but the man was saying, "The war with Germany is over . . ." The war was over . . . she couldn't believe it. But later that day it was repeated. People were out in the Crescent, full of jollity.

'Betty,' she asked, 'does this mean we can go home?'

'Yes, I think so,' Betty replied. Margaret's heart sang. *'I can go home to my mother and John,'* she kept thinking. Oh, what a lovely day.

Mrs Hall reiterated that the war was indeed pronounced over, and that no doubt arrangements would be made for the girls to go back home to London.

Margaret was beside herself. She started putting her things in each of the suitcases, then having to take items out to use them. She was looking forward to Mr Green coming and telling them they could go home. Even Betty became excited and kept dancing round the bedroom, doing mad things and not caring what Mrs Hall thought. Mrs Hall seemed to overlook some of the mischief that Betty was getting into.

It was some three weeks later that Mr Green called to see them. He told them that it was now safe for the girls to go home. Arrangements were being made, and he would call again and tell them when it was to be. Margaret ran to him, and he put his arm around her, she was crying tears of joy. She started packing in earnest, but it was to be some weeks before he called again.

Over the last few weeks the whole of Wrexham appeared to be whooping it up and rejoicing. There were lots of street parties, and in June the girls helped Mrs Hall prepare lots of food for the party in their Avenue. The shape of the Avenue was like a crescent, and the whole length was set with tables and chairs. There were pies and cakes, jellies and trifles. People brought out things they had been saving. Union Jacks began to appear on house fronts, and small ones were carried by lots of people, gaily waving them.

On the wireless it was stated that Mr Churchill had been mobbed by delirious crowds in Whitehall on VE Day (Victory in Europe). He had broadcast to the nation and to the empire:

> *The Evil doers are now prostrate before us. Our gratitude to our splendid allies goes forth from all our hearts in this island, and throughout the British Empire.*

VE Day was to be a Public Holiday.

VE Day itself dawned with dull skies and a slight drizzle. But even so, boisterous, rejoicing crowds were out everywhere. Then in the afternoon the sun came out. That evening street lights were switched on for the first time in London, and with all the economies, it was the first time in Wrexham. There were fireworks and bonfires in the parks. Margaret had never seen anything like it before.

*

School was just ending in July for the summer break when Margaret came home one afternoon to find Mr Green in the parlour, talking to Mrs Hall. He stood up as she entered the room, and not long afterwards Betty followed her in. Both girls sat down. Mr Green told them that Betty's parents were coming to Wrexham, by train, to collect her the following weekend. Betty jumped for joy. Margaret was apprehensive.

Mr Green said, 'Margaret, I have been telling Mrs Hall that you will be going home next week, all being well, with a lot of other children. Mrs Hall will take you to your old school on the other side of town, where you will join the coach. So if you make sure you pack all your things, I'll see you there on Tuesday morning at 9 o'clock. You will be getting on a coach which will be going all the way to London.'

Margaret got up and flung herself onto Mr Green's lap. Tears rolled down her face. How she loved and admired Mr Green, all the while she had been in Wrexham, he had taken a lot of time and trouble to see she was all right. Without him, she might still be with Mr and Mrs Jones.

He, on the other hand, appeared rather embarrassed with the child sitting on his lap, with her arms around him. He had been responsible for the welfare of lots of children who had been evacuated to this area, but Margaret had been special, and he was going to miss this shy, sad child.

But all Margaret could think about now was that at last she was really going home.

* * *

Chapter 10

Mr Green stayed for some while confirming all the arrangements, before getting up to leave. Margaret plucked up courage:

'Mr Green, thank you so much, I do love you,' she said to him.

'I'm very fond of you too Margaret, and I hope you will soon be reunited with your family,' he said. 'I am sure your mother will be delighted to have you home.

After he left, Mrs Hall couldn't have been nicer to the girls. She admitted she was going to miss them both. She didn't say she was going to miss the money she was paid to keep them. Margaret went to school the next day and said goodbye to everyone. School was closing down for the summer recess, and she would not be seeing Mrs Porter, or some of the other children ever again. She said a sad farewell to Judy, but made arrangements to see her at Church the following Sunday.

Everyone was excited. Other children in the school were going home also. Local people were so happy that the war was over, and that life would hopefully be going back to normal.

On Saturday she had to say farewell to Betty. Her parents arrived at lunchtime, they were all going back to London on the night train. They had to book their seats as there were so many people wanting to board the train.

The girls clung to each other, and wept. They had never been really good friends, they were so different, but they had endured eighteen months together living with Mrs Hall, which gave them some kind of bond.

Margaret went with Mrs Hall to see them off at the railway station. They had to travel by bus, standing up because the bus was so full. But nobody seemed to mind.

Margaret felt very bereft after they had gone and she was alone with Mrs Hall, knowing she was not leaving until Tuesday. But she was to learn that Mrs Hall had another side to her which had never shown itself before. She sat talking to Margaret downstairs and showed her photographs of her husband, who had died some years before. She brought boxes down from her bedroom and gave Margaret some little keepsakes.

There was a lovely little lace handkerchief, which was embroidered in one corner with flowers, which Mrs Hall had done herself many years ago. There was a little bottle of cologne perfume "4711" which smelt lovely, and a little book of poems, which Mrs Hall felt Margaret would like to have.

Margaret put her new treasures into one of her two suitcases. On Sunday she went to Church feeling elated that her prayers had finally been answered. She felt unhappy about it being the last time she would attend the church. She had many happy moments there, and liked so many of the people. She had to say goodbye to Judy, her friend, and also Judy's parents; as well as the vicar, and Mrs Brown.

Judy promised to write to her once Margaret had found out her new address in Richmond, where she would be living. She promised to write as soon as she could. It was all so sad. She was going to miss people. She knew she would always miss Mrs Perie, and she wondered where Pamela was now. Probably in America. She had never come to visit her, even though she had promised, but Margaret realised she must have been very busy, what with getting married, and sorting out the house.

No, life hadn't been so bad, although she wished with all her heart that she had had the opportunity to stay at Victoria Road for the whole of her time in North Wales.

*

Tuesday arrived at last. There was so much to do that morning. Although Margaret had packed everything days before, there were all the last minute little things. Her toothbrush, and her lovely hairbrush to squeeze into one of the cases. Tying on the labels Mr Green had given to Mrs Hall, which had her name and address on them. Margaret could see her name and the address to where she was going. "The Royal Hotel, Richmond Surrey". It sounded grand. Gosh, she would be there later today. She couldn't believe it.

She rushed next door and said goodbye to the neighbours, why she wasn't sure, she didn't like them that much, but it felt good to be doing it. Then on to the house further along, the nice couple who had taken her to church when she first arrived to live with Mrs Hall. Mr and Mrs Hughes were such kindly people, and gave Margaret some sweets to eat on her journey.

Then a last look round, before picking up one of her suitcases and a brown carry bag, which contained Mr Growler and her doll, Jane. Mrs Hall picked up her other case, and puffing and panting, they made their way to the bus stop just down the road.

It had been a struggle to board the bus. Other children were already on it, and the luggage compartment was full of bags and suitcases. They had to take the suitcases down the bus with them. Mrs Hall kept saying things to her, but she couldn't hear what she said because of the noise. So she just smiled and nodded.

They alighted near to the old school she had attended when she had lived in Victoria Road. It looked different somehow, possibly because it was closed for the summer holidays, but she didn't care at the moment. She lifted one of her cases and the bag, and walked across the playground, with Mrs Hall following more slowly behind. She was still puffing and panting. When they neared the table set up at the far end of the playground she noticed Mr Green was there, and also Miss Hindley, who she vaguely remembered she knew, but was not sure from where. Lots of children were arriving, and some were still having their labels tied on.

A lady had fastened her label onto a buttonhole of her dress. Everybody seemed happy, but there were also a lot of people crying. There were three big coaches in the school playground, Mrs Hall told her that she was going on coach 2. They made their way towards it. A man took the suitcases from them, but Margaret held on to the brown paper bag, which contained her teddy and doll. He inspected the labels, then placed the suitcases in the bottom of the coach.

Margaret bade farewell to Mrs Hall, and said she would miss her. Even though she had been nice these last few days, Margaret disliked her, in her heart of hearts. Mrs Hall was actually crying, and dabbing her eyes with a handkerchief.

All too soon, the children had their names called out, and were asked to board the coaches. The other two coaches were going to different places. Margaret's coach was going direct to London. Now that her mother had moved from Upminster she was going into the unknown, and one or two children she had recognised were getting onto another coach. She had no idea where she was going, and hoped somebody on the coach did. Was her mother going to meet her? She had no idea.

Mrs Hall stood next to the coach, and Margaret noted she had lit a cigarette; one of her favourite Woodbines. She would always remember Mrs Hall with a cigarette hanging out of the corner of her mouth, and that long ash, which never seemed to fall off the end, and what about the turban she often wore round her head covering her curlers, and the all-embracing pinny. No, she would never forget Mrs Hall.

Lots of chatter was all around her. She sat next to a girl who she discovered was called Amanda, who was about her own age. She had lovely blonde ringlets, and a beautiful face. She did look pretty. She also had a teddy bear with her.

The cheering and goodbyes were the order of the day as the coach finally pulled out of the school grounds. There was Mr Green standing by the entrance. A lump came into Margaret's throat, she would probably never see him again. How she admired him and was grateful for how he had cared about her. Yes, when she grew up she wanted to do a job like his.

Miss Hindley was on her coach and was walking up and down telling the children that they had to first go and pick up some children who were waiting at the bus station. The coach turned right and went along Bradley Road, and then turned into Grosvenor Road. Margaret knew where she was, she had often walked along these roads with Pamela Perie, when going into town. They passed the Moelor Hospital which she could see clearly as she was on the left side of the coach, and then the Borough Council Offices.

As they pulled into the bus station, she noticed a queue of children waiting with men and women, the children started to wave at the coach. There were more goodbyes to witness, and boys and girls clambering up the steep steps of the coach, and moving to the back seats which were still empty.

The coach started up once more, and this time went right through the centre of the town, through Hope Street, where there were some nice shops and where Pamela had bought some of her clothes to wear to school. The coach then turned right at Pen-y-Bryn Bridge, and along past the church she used to go with Pamela and Mrs Perie. Another lump came into Margaret's throat. She would never see Mrs Perie again, that lovely lady had died, and she would probably never see Pamela again as she had gone to America.

They drove along Ruabon Road, past the recreation ground where she had played on the swings and slides, and gradually they left the built up area of Wrexham behind them. The signposts said they were going towards Shrewsbury. This meant nothing to Margaret, she had never heard of it.

All she knew was that she was going home.

Finally the coach pulled out of Wrexham. Margaret was both sad and elated. It was what she had wanted for so long, but now that the moment had come she experienced a fear which she could not explain, as well as excitement to see her mother and John again.

The coach joined a very busy main road. As Margaret was near the front of the coach Miss Hindley, who was sitting just in front of her and next to the driver, told the children round her that they were on the main A5 road to London. They drove through Oswestry and Shrewsbury, and passed Telford, before approaching Birmingham. Margaret watched out of the window, fascinated with the vista of strange sounding places, and lots of countryside between each town.

There was a lot of chatter on the coach. Some of the younger children kept misbehaving, and Miss Hindley had to keep standing up and telling them off. But it was really high spirits.

Some of the older children were exchanging names and addresses with each other. Margaret thought about Mrs Hall waving goodbye to her as the coach had left the school. How she disliked the woman, who at the end had been so interesting and kind. How Margaret still hankered after the love and care given her by Mrs Perie and Pamela. They had not been her relatives but had been kindness itself. Oh, why had Mrs Perie needed to die? Just when things were going so well. She would never have had to stay with Mrs Hall at all.

Still, Mrs Hall had been better than Mrs Jones. Margaret shuddered at the thought of all the unkind things meted out to her at Salisbury Road. That awful little bed, how uncomfortable it had been, and eating that awful food out in the scullery all by herself. That awful Elizabeth Jones, always snubbing her, and going out of her way to show Margaret how inferior she was. She was welcome to her little bedroom, which she remembered so well, as she had had to clean it, and tidy it up so often for that horrid child.

The coach slowed down on the other side of Coventry, and pulled into a transport café, which was situated next to the road. Miss Hindley stood up and asked everybody to be quiet.

'Children, I want you to sit quietly and listen to me. We don't want to lose anyone, so please follow my instructions. We are all going to the toilet, and please make sure you go, as we do not stop again until we reach London. We are also going to have something to eat and drink. While we go into the toilets the driver will be getting out some orange juice and sandwiches to hand round. Is that clear?'

Everyone made noises that they had heard.

'Now please be as quick as you can, as we want to get going, so that we are in London before it gets dark.'

Miss Hindley moved to the door, which had mysteriously opened.

'Right now,' she said, 'stand up in twos and step down from the coach after me.' Miss Hindley stepped down.

Margaret and Amanda, the girl next to her, followed next.

During the first part of the journey Amanda had sat quietly with her teddy bear on her lap. She made it quite obvious that she didn't want to talk to anyone. Margaret had therefore accepted this, and had been happy to just look out of the window.

'Now we all stand still until everyone is off the coach,' Miss Hindley started to place people into a line. Then all the children were taken round the back of the café, and into a building which housed the toilets. They were rather grotty, and there was nowhere to wash your hands. 'Please keep together,' the good lady was saying, as the children emerged from the building and looked around them.

Margaret saw lots of big lorries and men dressed in overalls, all making a lot of noise and shouting. All dashing in and out of the café, and hurrying across the muddy ground. The children all stayed together, especially when one of the lorries started up its big engine and started to drive onto the road.

The children all trooped back to the coach. Of course there had to be someone missing. Miss Hindley took a count and had to leave the coach driver in charge whilst she returned to the building behind the café, and came back with young Billy Mitchell. She passed him up the coach steps, and told him to sit down at the front where she could see him.

The sandwiches were passed round, along with little paper cups of orange squash. When all was demolished, and all the rubbish tidied away, Miss Hindley once more took her seat, sending Billy Mitchell to his seat further down the coach. The coach started off once more. It was ten past twelve.

Some of the children became sleepy, and others were amusing themselves, either playing cat's cradle, or reading comics. The coach passed Towcester, then Leighton Buzzard, and on down the big road past St Albans.

As the coach neared London, all the countryside seemed to disappear, and everywhere was very built up. There were lots of houses, shops and factories. A lot of the buildings were in ruins. The coach passed through Kilburn. It was here that it turned off the main road. Miss Hindley shouted down the coach that some of the children would be getting out soon.

She had a list, which she consulted, and then went down the coach and told three children that in just a moment the coach would stop, and their parents would be there to meet them in St John's Wood. They started chatting noisily, waking up some children who had been asleep.

When the coach stopped, three children got off. Three lots of parents and relatives were waiting. Oh, the joy of homecoming. People laughing and crying. Everyone hugging and kissing each other.

The coach stopped again at Grays Inn, and despatched two more children to waiting relatives. The coach then turned right into the City of London. Margaret was fascinated with the big buildings. First there was St Paul's Cathedral, then Nelson's Column in Trafalgar Square, and then the Houses of Parliament. She had never seen them before.

Miss Hindley, although she was busy with her list, was also telling the children the names of the famous places, and a little bit of their history. Margaret liked Miss Hindley. She seemed to know so much, as well as being very kind to her. While she had been on the journey, Margaret had remembered that it had been Miss Hindley who had cared for her on the train when she had been going to North Wales, now some three years ago.

Amanda, sitting next to her, had become interested in the sights of London, or more appropriately, in awe of them. It was the first time she had said anything of consequence to

Margaret. As they passed Trafalgar Square she pointed to the stone lions and said, 'Aren't they big lions.'

Margaret said, 'I have never seen anything like it before.' Amanda smiled at Margaret, and told her that her mother was meeting her, but that her father had been killed in the war and she had been told by Mr Green that she would not see him any more.

Margaret felt sorry for her.

By the time they crossed the River Thames, half the children had already left the coach. Margaret had seen so many happy reunions from her seat at the front of the coach. She was beginning to get excited all over again. They were in London. The coach passed through Kennington, and past the Oval. She had heard her brother John talk about The Oval, they played cricket there.

The coach went back over the river, over Putney Bridge and down through Barnes. 'Gosh, Richmond was a long way. There were only six children on the coach now, besides herself. The coach stopped once more and Amanda started waving to some people on the pavement.

'That is my mother, and big sister,' she told Margaret.

Margaret joined in the excitement.

Amanda got off, carrying her teddy, and a brown carrier bag. The driver was getting a suitcase out of the bottom of the coach and handing it to the big girl next to Amanda. There were lots of cuddles and laughter. As the coach pulled away from the pavement, Margaret could see Amanda skipping along in front of everyone, obviously blissfully happy.

Just after Amanda left the coach it started raining. It had also started to get dark, partly because it was raining, though it was only 4 o'clock. The coach continued, Miss Hindley came and sat next to her. 'You are nearly home Margaret, I have been advised that your mother is working and is not able to meet the coach.' Margaret was mortified. Her mother was not coming to meet her. Surely she could have arranged to have some time off, even if it was just for a little while.

Still, never mind, Miss Hindley would take her to where her mother was working, and then they could go home together from there. She wondered where her mother lived, and where she herself was going to live.

Suddenly she was transfixed. She saw the sign. "The Royal Borough of Richmond upon Thames". They had arrived. Perhaps the Queen lived here.

* * *

Chapter 11

The coach pulled up outside the Town Hall. She became very nervous. She clung onto Mr Growler. Miss Hindley stepped down from the coach, and told Margaret to follow her. The coach driver had put her two suitcases on the pavement, and turning, told Miss Hindley that he would wait for her.

Miss Hindley picked up one of Margaret's suitcases for her while they made their way round the coach. They set off towards a large building. 'Your mother works here at the Royal Hotel my dear, we will go in through that door, and I'll leave you in the foyer while I go and find her.

Margaret went through the double doors, struggling with her suitcase and parcels, and stood looking around. It looked very plush. The walls were nicely painted and had "flock wallpaper" in a warm shade of red, covering large panels. The furniture looked rather old and comfy. It was rather dark in the foyer, and she was glad when she saw Miss Hindley returning, followed by, Yes . . . it was her mother . . . . She thought her heart would burst.

She left the suitcase and ran towards her. 'Mummy,' she cried. Her mother gave her a quick peck on the cheek, turned and thanked Miss Hindley for bringing her to the hotel, and then turned and asked a man who was coming out of a door on the right, to take the cases upstairs.

Miss Hindley said, 'Goodbye Margaret, I hope you soon settle in.'

Margaret waved, saying, 'Bye bye, and thank you.'

*

Mrs Trent told Margaret to follow her, and turned into the door on the right. People stared, they were mostly men. It was obviously a bar, and lots of men were drinking beer. Mrs Trent told Margaret she would have to sit in the room behind the bar, until she had finished work. She followed her mother behind the bar, and through another door. Inside it was very dark. There was an electric bulb hanging from the ceiling with no shade, and although it was alight it cast dark shadows all round the room. There were three wooden beer barrels placed around the room, and one centrally situated with a chair next to it.

'I'm afraid you will have to amuse yourself for quite a while, I work behind the snack bar, and I have some food to prepare,' her mother told her.

Margaret was just happy to be home. She would see John soon, she thought. She wished her mother had cuddled her, but she supposed it was because there were so many people about, and she was working. *No, it probably wouldn't be right,* she thought.

'It's all right, I'll sit here and do some drawing,' she told her mother. She had a little drawing book and pencils in her carrier bag, and had not used them on the journey, because there had been so much to see.

She sat on the chair, and her mother disappeared. She came back a little while later, with a glass containing lemonade. 'Here, have a drink Margaret, you must be thirsty,' she said. Margaret thanked her.

Margaret sat there for what seemed ages. She was getting very bored. She had completely filled up her little book, and there was nothing else to do. She had looked forward to coming home, and she felt so lonely in the little room, which was so very gloomy.

Suddenly she jumped out of her skin. She saw something move across the floor. She thought at first she must have been mistaken. Then, there it was again. 'A Rat!'

she screamed, and jumped up onto the barrel. Her mother came running in.

She looked so worried. 'What's the matter,' she cried.

Margaret stared at the space where the rat had been. 'Oh Mummy, there was a rat, it ran across the room. I'm frightened, please take me away.'

'You silly girl,' her mother said. 'They won't hurt you, they don't usually come out when it is light in here.' She went on, 'They are more scared of you. You must be quiet, or you will get me into trouble and I'll lose my job.'

Margaret continued to sit on the barrel. She sat there, terrified. It was some time later that her mother came and fetched her to take her upstairs. Margaret followed her mother dutifully.

'Did you have a nice journey?' she asked the child.

'It was a long way, and I'm very hungry,' Margaret replied.

'I'll start the dinner now,' her mother said. 'There are some packets of crisps in the cupboard, which should keep you going until we eat.'

Margaret opened the cupboard her mother had indicated and took out a bag of Smith's crisps. She opened it up and took out the little blue paper twist of salt and sprinkled it generously over the contents.

'Where is John, Mummy?' she asked.

'Oh, he is working in London, and may not return before you go to bed,' she replied. Margaret was disappointed, as she had so looked forward to seeing her brother.

'What does he do Mummy?' she asked.

'Oh, he works at the Stock Exchange, I don't know exactly what he does there,' her mother replied.

When she had followed her mother upstairs she had found herself some three floors up. She was quite out of puff by the time she came to the wide landing. Her mother stopped outside a door marked No 2, and put a key in the lock. On entering she found herself in a narrow passage, which had five doors leading off.

Carrying her crisps with her she investigated all the doors. There were two rooms with beds in, a small bathroom and toilet, a sitting room and the kitchen, where her mother was busy preparing a meal. As she entered the kitchen she was thinking what a tiny place it was for all of them, and nothing like the house in Upminster.

Her mother's voice cut through her thoughts. 'Come and help me lay the table, there's a good girl.'

Margaret was used to laying the table and she soon found the necessary cutlery drawer and the tablecloth. She laid two places, but when her mother looked at the table she said, 'Oh no, there are four of us.'

Margaret blinked. 'Four!'

Her mother went on, 'I'll introduce you to Ted in a little while, and John will eat later this evening.' Her mother saw the questions in her daughter's face.

'Who is Ted?' Margaret ventured.

Her mother replied, 'He is a friend of mine, and he lives here. He is the under manager of this hotel.' Margaret was stunned. Her mother went on, 'He is very nice, and is hoping to buy a house for us all some time soon, that will be nice, won't it?'

Margaret found her voice. 'Have you married him?'

'Oh no dear,' her mother replied, I haven't planned on getting married again, but I needed some company, and someone to help me. Your sister suggested it, and I'm grateful to her.' Her mother went on, 'You remember before you went to North Wales we went to Clacton, and I introduced you to Ted?'

Margaret thought for a moment, and then she remembered. She recalled going to Clacton on the train, and her mother had told her they were going to the seaside for the day, but she never saw the sea, and the promised paddle, and play with the sand, had never came to fruition. Instead she had stayed at some strange place. Yes, she remembered the man her mother had talked to. *Oh no, not him surely.* She hadn't liked him, even though he had bought her an ice cream and some sweets. He had kept smiling at her. *Oh no, not him!*

She was still thinking of that visit when the front door of the flat opened, and in he came.

He came forward towards her and said, 'Hello Margaret, how nice to see you after such a long time. How did you like North Wales?'

She swallowed, 'I didn't like it much, and I'm glad to be home.'

'Well, you should like it here,' he said, 'but there won't be much for you to do while your mother is working.'

She thought of the little dark room she had just left. Surely she wouldn't have to go back in there. She could stay in the flat.

Ted went on, 'I don't want you to be lonely, I've got an idea.' She didn't know what he was talking about; but said nothing. Ted chatted on to her mother about something that had happened earlier in the day, and Margaret started to wonder where to put her things. Her suitcases were still in the hallway. She sat down, and wondered what to do. Her excitement of being home had started to wane.

Her mother was busy preparing the dinner, and just before they sat down to dinner at the table, in walked her brother John. Once more she was ecstatic. He smiled at her.

'Hi sis,' he greeted her. 'Gosh I'm tired.' He went on looking at her, 'How was Wales?'

'Oh John, it was nothing like you said, I didn't like it, except when I stayed with Mrs Perie.'

John nodded, but seemed distracted, and this left Margaret feeling bereft. She had so been looking forward to seeing him, and envisaged him sweeping her into his arms, and them going off on their own to talk non-stop together about the past three years. Surely he was pleased to see her. She looked at him. He had changed. He was taller, and wore a grey flannel suit, which she later learnt he had bought at the Fifty Shilling Tailors in Richmond. He did look smart, and his hair was now slicked back, but he looked nervous all the while.

But where was the happy reunion? Her mother's welcome had consisted of a peck on the cheek, and putting her into the little dark room. Even though they had come up to the flat there were still no comforting cuddles, or words, saying how she had been missed. Perhaps they hadn't missed her. Her mother was probably too busy with Ted to care about her. John sat down and ate his dinner, and then flaked out in a chair.

She suddenly remembered Bobbie. 'John, you wrote and told me Bobbie had died, what was the matter with him?'

John opened one eye and said, 'Oh, mum had him put down when we moved, she couldn't bring him here to the flat.'

Tears welled up in her eyes, Bobbie hadn't died, he had been put down. She wouldn't be able to cuddle up to him like she used to. He had understood when she was unhappy. The tears spilled down her cheeks. How could her mother have done such a thing? John got up and came over to her.

'There, don't cry like that, you should be happy you are home.'

'I am glad I'm home,' she replied, choking on her tears, but I can't believe Mum would have Bobbie put down.' She could picture the dog, with his lovely soft coat, wagging his tail, and getting excited when she went near him. She had loved crawling into his kennel, and he seemed happy to share it with her. A sanctuary. She would have loved to go there now. Things were not as she thought they would be.

Gone was the house she remembered, her nice little bedroom and the lovely garden, and in its place was this tiny flat. Her mother was busy, and seemed to have no time for her. John was working, and didn't come home until late, and also he seemed to have changed. He had grown up, and was off hand with her. Then there was Ted. She hadn't bargained on someone else living with them. Still, she was home.

That night she had to sleep on the settee in the living room. Her mother had told her they had not had any time to sort things out. On the other hand where could she sleep. There were only two bedrooms. John had one, which was very tiny, and only had room for a small single bed and a chest of drawers, and her mother and Ted had the other. Yes, there was definitely one large bed in her mother's room. Her mother had said she was not considering marrying Ted, but she was sleeping with him. Her two cases still stood in the small hall, unpacked. There was nowhere to put her things. After a tiring day, and a wealth of emotions, she finally fell into a deep sleep on the sofa.

The following morning she discovered that neither her mother nor Ted worked first thing in the morning, and did not get up until after nine o'clock. John had already left to catch his train to London. She had not heard him get up, or leave. But his bed was empty.

At breakfast Ted smiled at Margaret, and said, 'We are going out to Twickenham this morning, I have a surprise for you.' She wasn't impressed, but she was anxious to find out what it was. After clearing up the breakfast things, and getting dressed, they left the flat, walking downstairs and through the hotel. She hadn't counted yesterday, but today she realised they must be right at the top of the building, after descending four flights of stairs. There was no lift. They went out into the main road, where they caught a bus not far from the hotel. It was only a short journey, which took them over Richmond Bridge, spanning the River Thames.

Ted took them to a little shop, which had lot of little animals in cages in the window. Her mother was very quiet, and appeared disinterested in the trip.

Margaret followed Ted inside, and immediately she started to stroke the little kittens and rabbits. What lovely little fluffy bundles they were. Ted picked up a little puppy, he was brown and had a patch over his right eye.

'Here Margaret, how would you like to own him?' he asked her.

Margaret's eyes opened wide. 'Oh, he is lovely, can I really have him?' she cried. A dog of her own! Little was she aware of the difficulties which lay ahead. Her mother looked none too pleased. She showed the little puppy to her mother. 'Look Mummy, isn't he adorable?' Her mother agreed he looked very cute.

Ted went over and paid the man behind the counter, and bought a little dog basket, a collar and a lead. They put the collar on. He looked so funny, the collar looked much too big for him, but it was the smallest one in the shop. Ted said he would make it smaller when they got home.

Margaret cuddled the puppy all the way home on the bus. He seemed to like being close to her, and his nose was so very cold. She put the lead on him when they alighted from the bus, and he scampered all over the place. Eventually, she decided to pick him up and carry him.

Once back in the flat she discovered that the puppy kept wetting the carpet. Little wet patches could be found, as the puppy excitedly ran round, finding out where he was. Her mother kept chasing him into the kitchen where the floor was covered in linoleum.

Ted had disappeared downstairs. Her mother stated, 'You'll have to clean up after him, and keep him in the kitchen until he is trained. We can't have him keep wetting the carpet in the sitting room. Margaret didn't mind at first, she had someone of her own. He wasn't exactly Bobbie, but he was warm and soft and cuddly.

Yes, she already loved the little puppy, who constantly licked her. She decided to call him Patch, as he had a patch over one eye. He was just a little mongrel really, but in Margaret's eyes he was beautiful, and so cute. She loved him. Ted had given the impression that buying the puppy had bought her friendship. How wrong could he be!

The Royal Hotel was right next to the River Thames, and each day Margaret took Patch for a walk up and down the towpath, sometimes as much as three or four times a day. She discovered that this kept her out of the little dark room behind the bar. Her mother was not happy leaving her in the flat, so when she was not walking the puppy, she often spent quite some time in the barrel room, as she came to call it.

Before the bar was opened each day she was allowed behind the bar, and used to help her mother making up potato salad. Patch however, was not allowed downstairs, and had to stay in the little kitchen upstairs, where his basket had been put.

Her mother was not happy about leaving him in the flat either. They sometimes returned to find not only had he made a mess, but that he had chewed things with his sharp little teeth. He was not popular with her mother, but Ted always stroked him and laughed at his mischief and funny antics . . . that is until the day he chewed through Ted's shoelaces, when he was immediately admonished for bad behaviour.

So taking Patch for a walk regularly became almost an obsession. It kept her out of the little dark room, and Patch out of mischief.

Schools were still on the summer holiday break, so the days stretched long, and empty. She knew no one, and most evenings John did not return from London much before 7 o'clock. Occasionally he didn't come in at all. Margaret didn't like sleeping on the couch, it was becoming most uncomfortable, and Mr Growler took up quite a lot of room. Not that she would ever consider him being anywhere else. He was the one person who had been everywhere with her in the past three years.

*

Two or three weeks passed, then one day Ted told them all that things had become desperate, and they needed more space urgently, so he had bought a house for them all in Mortlake, not far from Richmond. That day they went to see it. They took a bus, then they had to walk some distance to 43 Kingsway, which happily wasn't too far.

Margaret loved the house at first sight. There was a crab apple tree in the front garden, and as they entered the front door she had the illusion of space. After being cramped up in the flat for three weeks, and not having a bedroom of her own, she was looking forward to coming to live at the house.

Her mother and Ted were busy talking together and making plans, which gave her the opportunity to look around. The hallway went straight through the house downstairs, and there were doors off. The first one was a large room, with a fireplace, and nice wallpaper with pretty flowers all over. There were great big windows overlooking the front garden. She could envisage big armchairs in there. She closed the door behind her and moved along to the next door. This was a smaller room, completely empty, but it had French doors, which led out into the back garden. Probably this could be the dining room.

She continued down the passage and into the kitchen, and then the scullery where a large brown stone sink stood. Her mother was asking Ted if the "utility room" could be renovated in some way.

She opened the back door and went out into the garden. There was a large expanse of lawn, and half way along was a pond with lily leaves splayed across the water. She ran right down to the bottom of the garden, where there was a high railing, to discover that there was a railway line running along behind. She ran back indoors, passing some wooden steps leading up to the back bedroom, and at the top was a little veranda outside the doors. Honeysuckle grew up the side of the steps, it smelt lovely. There was also an outside toilet.

Margaret went back into the house and ran upstairs. Her mother and Ted were already upstairs, and her mother told her that the little back bedroom was to be hers. *Oh super,* she thought. This was the room that had little French doors that led out onto the veranda. A bedroom of her own at last. She was thrilled.

There were two other bedrooms. The big front bedroom was to be for her mother and Ted, and the other bedroom for John. Oh, this was much better.

They returned to the Royal Hotel, and started packing. Lots of tea chests were delivered, and Margaret helped her mother pack the china and ornaments and place them in the packing cases. The house that Ted had purchased had vacant possession, so they could move in straight away.

Two days before they left the flat to live in the house, her elder sister May came to visit them and brought her two young children with her. Terry was just three years old, and his younger brother Clive was just a baby. Her mother made quite a fuss of the children. Terry was into everything.

May welcomed her home from Wales, but Margaret was mostly ignored by both her mother and her sister. She went and played with her doll Jane, and then decided to take Patch for a walk. Terry had been continually tormenting the little dog for some time. She fetched his lead and went into the kitchen, but found he wasn't there. She looked into the living room, behind the chairs, where he often hid, but he wasn't there either. She looked in the bedrooms, but could not find him anywhere. Where could he be?

She began to get really worried.

* * *

Chapter 12

She went back into the kitchen and asked her mother, 'Mummy, have you seen Patch, I can't find him anywhere?' Her mother turned round from the sink and said, 'No, I haven't seen him for some while, but he must be somewhere. He was out here under my feet some time ago. Go and look again, he is probably hiding somewhere from the boys.' Her mother returned to talking to her sister, having dismissed her.

She heard her mother say, 'That dog is more trouble than it is worth. Ted should never have bought it for her.'

May said, 'The flat is too small to have a dog cooped up here, but I suppose it is company for the child, and you will be moving in the next few days to Mortlake, where there will be more space. Perhaps you could put a kennel in the back garden for him.'

Her mother replied, 'I will be glad when we move, there was never enough room before Margaret came home from North Wales, but now it is impossible. Margaret has to sleep on the sofa, and the flat is always so cluttered. Ted and I have no time to ourselves now either. John's at work, but Margaret is always here.'

Margaret slipped out of the kitchen unnoticed, and continued searching for her little dog. *'I don't think Mummy wanted me to come home,'* she thought. Tears rolled down her cheeks. She was obviously in the way, and a nuisance. No one wanted her, not her mother, nor she supposed Ted, and John was always too busy; she had no friends, and nowhere to go each day. She would be glad when they moved and when she started school in September.

Oh, where was Patch, she needed him to cuddle and listen to her. But no amount of searching either in the flat or around the hotel made any difference. All day long she called his name and hunted right through the hotel. It was such a big building. She thoroughly checked all the three bars, along the long corridor which led into the ballroom. She loved the ballroom with its shiny polished floor, and the delicate little chairs and tables which were placed all around the outside of the big room. She scoured the kitchens, where she thought he might have gone looking for food, and also the empty dining room. Margaret walked along the river bank in both directions, going to all the places she had walked with him, but Patch was nowhere to be found.

That night she couldn't sleep, and she cried buckets, pining for her dog. Oh, where could he be? The following morning the search began again, but later that day she heard her mother and sister talking:

'I found the front door open yesterday, just before Margaret said she couldn't find that wretched puppy,' her mother was saying.

May said, 'Terry is always opening doors, you could be right, he might have opened the door thinking the dog wanted to go out.'

Her mother went on, 'I can't say I'm sorry, he was always wetting on the floor, and the flat was beginning to smell. I don't want that at the house, as we are going to have new carpets, do I?' May appeared to nod, and agree with her mother. Margaret was distraught. Her little dog was missing, and everyone seemed to be glad he had gone. How could they? He was so sweet. She had always cleared up after him, even though she hated doing it.

She mourned her little dog for days, wondering where he was. Had he been run over? He was so silly crossing the road.

Her sister and the two boys went back to London, and she was busy putting her last things together once more, and helping her mother packing still more china and books, ready for the move to Mortlake. She had been looking forward to going to the house, but now that Patch was missing, all her enthusiasm had vanished.

She didn't really want to leave the flat in case he came back looking for her. She was so miserable. She had so looked forward to coming home from North Wales, but nothing was right, and she kept reflecting on how happy she had been with Mrs Perie. She had been a lovely lady. How she missed her now. Mrs Perie would have listened to her, and tried to find the dog, she was sure. John seemed off-hand about him too, his opinion was that the puppy would show up sometime, and Ted and their mother were still going to work at the hotel, so when Patch turned up they could come and collect him.

Moving day arrived. Her brother John had been able to get the day off from work. A big lorry arrived at the back door of the hotel, and three men gradually loaded the furniture and the tea chests, full of items, onto the lorry. Their mother cleaned up after they had gone, and then they all set off by bus to Mortlake.

When they arrived, all the rooms had furniture and boxes in them. Ted had stayed at the hotel, as he was working, John had to sweep all the floors before items were gradually put into place. A van arrived with two men carrying in rolls of linoleum and carpets. Margaret was told to find the box with the bed linen and to make up the beds as soon as they were fixed together. John's bed was easy to do, and so was the little second hand bed they had bought for her, but making up the big double bed she found most difficult, and had to keep running round from side to side, to tuck in the sheets and blankets.

Her mother did not have to go to work for two days, and that afternoon all three of them worked hard putting things in their places around the house.

By the time they had to prepare the evening meal she was exhausted. She wanted to just flake out on her bed. She went up to her little room. It was rather sparse, but it was hers. There had not been enough carpet for her bedroom so she had been given a little old rug to put beside her bed. The rest of the floor was dark stained bare boards. She had a little washstand, which she knew had come from the house in Upminster, which had a little cupboard where she could put her clothes, and two little drawers above where she could put her Bible, her hair slides and ribbons. She placed her hairbrush on the top, and put Mr Growler in her bed.

She loved the view of the garden through the little doors. Her mother had said that she should keep the doors closed, why, she didn't know. She had noticed that her chest of drawers was in the big bedroom and her mother had put some of Ted's clothes in it. She felt quite resentful that she couldn't have her own chest of drawers.

The two days flew by, there was so much to do. A new three-piece suite was delivered and put into the sitting room. Two armchairs, and a three-seater settee, all covered with apple green velvet, it was lovely. The family piano took pride of place, and Margaret learned that she was to start piano lessons in September. She was thrilled. She had always wanted to be able to play like John. Her brother was already an accomplished pianist, and her older sister, May, played the piano when she visited. Her mother had often implied how well her sister had played, and continually grumbled that she had given it all up to marry that "so and so" she called a husband.

May's husband was a lowly rating in the Royal Navy, and when on shore leave he was usually drunk. He also used to beat her sister up whilst he was under the influence of alcohol. Her mother had a very low opinion of him. Having said that, she also often commented that May had got all that she deserved, having run away from home and got herself pregnant so that it had become necessary for her to marry Alf in the first place. May had been a "nippy" waitress in one of the Lyons Corner Houses up in London, and Alf had come along and swept her off her feet. Since the children had been born she had been regretting her hasty decisions, and often came and told her mother what she had to put up with. Mother showed little sympathy, but at the same time was quite supportive, and allowed May to come to stay at times.

So now she herself was going to learn to play the piano. If she played it well, perhaps her mother would like her better. Since her return from North Wales Margaret had been yearning for her mother to show her some affection, but she was always too busy. She made Margaret feel she was in the way, and implied that the child caused so many problems.

Margaret wondered who would look after her while her mother worked, bearing in mind it was some 8 miles from Richmond, or whether she would have to go with her mother each day and stay in the little dark room behind the bar more often.

She learnt that as well as learning to play the piano, she was going to have the opportunity to learn ballet, and tap dancing, as well as attend elocution lessons. She was so excited, she had always wanted to learn to dance, and loved seeing ballet dancers in their pretty tutus. She believed her mother was paying for everything. It would be some time before she learnt that Ted had paid for everything. Perhaps their relationship would have been better had she known; on the other hand, she resented anything he did for her. He had taken the one thing she wanted, and that was her mother's love.

How she hated Ted! Her mother had no time for her when Ted was about. He was always complaining about her leaving the electric lights on, and drinking milk from the larder. Her mother always appeased Ted. When he implied things went missing from the larder, her mother put a lock on the door; then there were the times he switched the bathroom light off whilst she was still in the bath (the switch was outside the bathroom door), and if she told her mother, she was told, 'You shouldn't have had it on so long, electricity costs money.'

How she missed Patch, he would have loved the garden. He could have fun around out there, and not been in her mother's way, and he would have been safe, as there was a high fence all round the garden. How she mourned the loss of the little dog. He had never been found.

*

One day her mother came home from work and told her that they were going on a journey to Scotland. She listened to what her mother said in trepidation. Surely she wasn't going away again. John had implied she might be sent away if she was naughty, whilst they were still living in the hotel flat. During the past few days, while she had been left at home in the house, she had been positive she had not been naughty. She had mainly played quietly on her own, or sat reading a book. She had also written some poems. She liked poems. Mrs Perie had often read her some lovely poetry.

No, her mother was quite clear, just Margaret and her mother were going to visit relatives near Edinburgh in Scotland. Margaret didn't know who they were. She had never been to Scotland, and she could not remember anyone from there visiting the family.

'Who are they, Mummy?' she asked.

Her mother explained that her father belonged to the Trent Clan, and there were aunts, uncles and cousins living in Pencaitland, and East Lothian. Her great aunt lived in Fife. 'Your aunt Clara has invited us to go for a holiday for two weeks, and as you do not start school until the second week in September, I felt it would be opportune. I had been invited to visit just after your father died, but was unable to travel because of the war, as well as I had insufficient money to go. We are going to travel up on the "Royal Scot".'

Gosh, she had been home just a few weeks from North Wales, and here she was going to Scotland.

Out came her battered suitcase again, and in went her best clothes. Ted had bought her another dress, and a pair of shoes. Her mother told her that Ted had to remain working at the hotel, and John had to continue to work also. She would have her mother all to herself!

Margaret was still a little apprehensive, she hadn't forgotten that Betty had told her that her parents had taken her to Wales and left her with the Aunt Ann for two years. Even though her mother had said they would be coming back for her to start school nothing could dispel the worry she felt.

However, there was much excitement, and her mother made the final preparations, and two days later they set off by train from Mortlake to Waterloo Station. Once more she was in the big city, which looked even larger from the pavement than when she had seen it from her seat on the coach, returning from Wales.

They caught a bus, which made its way across London, and finally they arrived at Euston Station.

She recalled the last time she had entered Euston Station some three years before, with all the other children. As they entered the big station memories flooded back. How lonely she had been when she had boarded the train for Wales, and everyone had been so sad, saying goodbye.

The station was still very busy, and lots of servicemen were rushing around, but the atmosphere was so much happier. Things were somehow different for her now. Her mother was with her, and she also had a suitcase. She looked around, marvelling at all the people running around and shouting everywhere, but the depressed attitude of people that she had witnessed before seemed to have disappeared. The atmosphere was almost of gaiety, although there were still people saying goodbye and clinging to each other, especially near the big trains.

Her mother secured the services of a porter for the two cases, and followed him towards one of the big steam trains. As they passed the big engine, Margaret could see that lots of smoke was coming from the funnel on the top. Along the side of the great machine were the words "The Royal Scot". She thought, *It must be costing a lot of money to be going to Scotland.*

She accompanied her mother along the platform, and boarded the train. They found some seats near the dining car. It was then that Margaret was to learn from her mother that her eldest brother William, who had been in the Royal Air Force, was now working on the Royal Scot as a steward.

Since returning from Wales she had only seen John and her sister May, and she had heard nothing about William or Robbie. No one had mentioned them.

William came towards them, having come through a doorway, and was soon in conversation with her mother. She overheard that he had booked a table in the dining car for 12.30 pm, for them both. Her mother seemed pleased. It was obvious to anyone that she doted on her eldest son, and when in conversation with another couple who had joined them in their carriage, she was quick to inform them that her son was the steward of the dining car.

Margaret sat quietly looking out of the window as the train pulled out of the station, and gradually got up speed, heading north. Her apprehension and fear was mingled with happiness and excitement. She wondered about the people she was going to see, and if she would like them. How was it that these relatives were unknown? Her mother told her during the journey that she had been named Margaret after her cousin Margaret who lived in East Lothian, and that her cousin was training to be a nurse. Margaret was keen to see her namesake.

Some two hours passed, and gradually she became bored. It was obviously a long way. Her mother continually talked with the couple opposite her, and learned that they had lost a son in the fighting on the Normandy beaches, and they also were visiting relatives up north.

Her mother's opinion was that little girls should be seen and not heard, so she mostly made herself inconspicuous, sitting quietly reading or looking out of the window at the scenery.

Eventually her brother came through the doorway and told them it was time to have lunch. She was much relieved to be doing something, and she was also hungry. They followed him along the corridor, and into the dining car, where a table was laid for two.

The silver cutlery and the glassware sparkled. She was offered a menu, but her mother decided what she would have. The first course arrived, they both had soup, and Margaret found it difficult to lift the spoonful of soup to her mouth, as each time the train gave little jolts, the liquid would drop over the side of the spoon, and she was scared of dropping some on her lap. But she managed, and William came and removed the empty plates. Although rationing was still in force, there was obviously no shortage on the train.

Another large plate was put in front of her, and gradually William placed slices of roast lamb with mint sauce on the plate, and added various vegetables, including some *pommes frites,* little soft balls of potato, deep fried. She had never had them before. Her mother had commented that they were not worth the money, which seemed quite a cynical view when they tasted so nice.

William once more removed the plates when they had finished the main course. She was allowed ice cream for sweet, which came in a little silver scoop dish. Oh, what a lovely meal!

The couple sitting across the gangway seemed too busy talking and absorbed in each other to eat much. The lady was a very pretty girl, and the man was in sailor uniform. They kept holding hands across the table, Margaret kept looking at them until her mother finally told her to stop it, and that it was rude to stare.

Her mother finished off with a cup of tea, and Margaret had a small glass of orange squash. Afterwards, they returned to their seats in the carriage, as the train continued to thunder on towards Scotland. Margaret felt very sleepy, and gradually she fell asleep with Mr Growler on her lap.

She woke with a start. Her mother was standing up and retrieving a bag from the luggage rack. She told Margaret to get her things together as they had arrived in Edinburgh. It was dark outside the train. As they stepped down onto the platform, William appeared and went to fetch a porter to take their luggage, before getting back on the train himself. They followed the porter along the platform and through the station exit. Her mother looked round. Margaret stood close to her.

Suddenly, a tall young man, who was extremely thin, came towards them. He wore a brown trilby hat, and a grey suit. He looked extremely smart, although the brown suede shoes looked distinctly out of place. He approached her mother, lifting his trilby hat.

Her mother obviously knew him. He greeted her warmly saying, 'Hello Aunt Jane, did you have a good journey?'

She put her cheek up for him to kiss her and replied, 'It has been a long journey, but William made us comfortable, and we had a very nice lunch.'

He lightly kissed her cheek and then turned round to Margaret. 'And this must be Margaret, welcome to Scotland, I hope you have a pleasant stay.'

The word "stay" conjured up her fears, but she greeted him by saying hello. She felt very shy of him. He was very good looking. He bent and lightly kissed her cheek, saying, 'I'm your cousin Angus, it's lovely to see you.'

He took the suitcases from the porter and tipped him. He said, 'Follow me Aunt Jane, I have a car outside the station.'

Her mother followed him, and Margaret trailed along behind. Outside the station was a little black car, just like the one Mr Green had driven in North Wales. Angus put the cases in to the car on the back seat, and Margaret sat next to them. Her mother sat in the front next to Angus.

He started the car with the turning handle before getting in himself. He put the handle on the floor of the car. While he edged his way out of the station and along through the big city, he chatted away to her mother, asking her more about the journey, and then told them that the weather was promising for the next two weeks from what he had heard, and he wished them a pleasant stay.

They drove right through Edinburgh, along Princes Street. Margaret could see the huge castle high up at one end. She admired the beautiful floral mile, where hundreds of flowers were arranged into patterns, and a lovely floral clock. She could make them out quite clearly even though it was dark. They drove out into the countryside, and eventually turned into the gates of a tiny cottage.

'Here we are,' Angus said, 'it is a bit small, but it is very comfortable.'

It really was small, with little windows and a main front door. There were very few flowers in the little front garden but it was well tended. They walked through the front door, Angus following with the cases. Margaret was fascinated. The living room was large, and in two alcoves were beds made up with curtains half pulled across them. The large table in the middle of the room was covered by a big thick cloth, and standing on the top was a large oil lamp. As it was now very dark outside the lamp was lit.

No electricity!

Her Aunty Clara greeted them warmly. She was Angus's mother. Tea was made and waiting for them and consisted of little flat griddle scones which were hot from the stove, and fruitcake, all home made. This was followed by steaming mugs of hot chocolate.

By the time everything was eaten, and all cleared away it was time for Margaret to go to bed. She was put in one of the beds in the corner. It was a very soft mattress. Her mother said it was made from feathers. She was soon undressed behind the big curtain, which had been pulled right across the corner, so that she had a little room all to herself. She was soon fast asleep. It had been a very long day.

*

The following morning Margaret was up early. The cockerel was crowing at dawn, and lots of unusual sounds met her ears. Margaret got up and dressed. *Where do you wash?* she asked herself. In the end she just put her clothes on and went outside. It was just light, and she could see for miles. So this was Pencaitland.

She walked down the lane and saw two other cottages just like her aunt's. In the fields nearby she could see lots of chickens roaming around, pecking at the ground. There was a goat tethered to the ground, and one field had sheep standing together as if waiting for something. One far field had lots of cows all huddled into a corner near the gate.

She thought she had better retrace her steps in case anyone wondered where she was. She returned to her aunt's cottage to be met by Angus who was now up and busy washing his hands and face. She hadn't noticed before that there was a water tap just outside the back door, and Angus was drawing off some water by pumping a big handle up and down.

'Hello Margaret, did you sleep well?' he asked her.

'Yes thank you Angus,' she replied.

'Would you like to come with me to the farm just along the lane?' he asked, 'I am going to get some milk in this churn, as we will need some for breakfast.'

'Ooh, yes please,' she cried. It sounded fun.

And it was. He took her past the other two cottages, and opened a big gate enough for them to walk through, making sure he closed it after them, and walked towards the milking sheds. He greeted the farmer, Jim Hurst. 'Good morning Jim,' said Angus, 'I've brought my cousin Margaret to show her the cows and to get some milk.'

'Very good, mind your feet Margaret, it is a bit muddy here on the farm,' he told her.

Margaret suddenly realised her best shoes were covered in mud. What would her mother say? But Angus seemed unconcerned, and took her into the milking shed, where several cows were waiting to be milked. It was fascinating. She watched while the farmer attached some tubes to the underside of a cow. Then he started to pull something. She wasn't sure what was happening, but she could see that some milk was going into a pail underneath.

'Would you like to try?' Angus asked her.

'Oh no, I don't think so,' she replied. She was nervous about touching the big animals and she didn't fancy touching those things hanging down, which were right underneath the cow. Oh no.

They went over to the farmhouse afterwards, and collected some milk that had settled and was ready for drinking, and carried a small churn back to the cottage, as well as some butter.

What an experience. Margaret ran ahead of Angus and rushed into the cottage to tell her mother where she had been. Her mother responded, and appeared interested in all the child was telling her, until she looked down and saw Margaret's shoes, when she turned to Margaret and said, 'Take those shoes off and clean them, you'll make a mess everywhere, they are covered in mud.'

Angus who had come in and heard the remark said, 'Don't fret Aunt Jane, the floors are made of flag stones, and are used to it. Here Margaret, give me your shoes, and I'll take them outside and clean them for you. You really need a pair of Wellington boots like mine.'

She took them off and gave them to him. The floor was very cold. She liked Angus, he was very nice. Her Aunt Clara liked him too, she could tell.

After a hearty breakfast of porridge made with the milk they had brought, also some eggs and bacon with toast and real marmalade which Aunt Clara had made herself, Angus told them he would take them into Edinburgh to see it properly in the daylight.

He drove the little car through the country lanes, and pointed out little things of interest, until they finally parked in a side street and got out of the car, and walked into Princes Street. Her mother bought her some Edinburgh Rock. It was very sweet and chalky tasting, but it was nice. Her mother had been extremely kind to her during the trip, since leaving the train and William. She had shown a great deal of interest in anything Margaret said or did, and had affectionately tucked her into bed last night. The child had been overjoyed about this turn of events. Perhaps her mother did love her after all.

Angus took them to Edinburgh Castle, and they toured the battlements and watched the soldiers, in their kilts and Busby hats, marching. They looked so resplendent, and some of the soldiers were playing bagpipes. Margaret was fascinated.

They walked back down the hill, and along Princes Street, passing the beautiful floral arrangements, which she could now see clearly in all their glory. There was a bracing wind, but the weather was fine. She kept her coat buttoned right up to her neck, and her beret firmly sitting on her head. Aunt Clara had lent her a big scarf to wear to make sure she kept warm.

They had stopped to have some lunch at a little restaurant which was situated upstairs above one of the shops. They had a beautiful view of the castle from the front windows.

On the journey home to the cottage, Margaret reminisced about the lovely food. Angus had insisted on treating them. Her mother had chosen Scotch broth to start with, followed by home made Steak and Kidney Pie and vegetables. It had been delicious. The little crème caramel puddings had tasted out of this world. She had really enjoyed her day in Edinburgh.

The following day Angus took her blackberry picking. They went out walking for what seemed miles, and collected lots of berries from the hedgerows, so that Aunt Clara could make blackberry and apple pies and puddings. Her aunt was a good cook.

One morning Angus took her to pick some mushrooms. He told her the night before that he would have to call her really early the following morning as the mushrooms were best picked while they were open, before 6 am. So the next morning he shook her gently and told her it was time to go. It was still very dark outside, but she followed him stealthily, carrying a basket in which to put the mushrooms. He showed her which ones to pick, and before long the basket was full.

They carried them home, where a delighted Aunt Clara immediately cooked half of them for breakfast, which accompanied potato scones, already cooking on the griddle.

Margaret enjoyed every moment at the cottage.

During the second week relatives of her father's, who she didn't know at all, came to see her mother. They took her mother to see other family members, while Margaret stayed with Aunt Clara. One day Angus took them to Fife to see Aunt Amy and her daughter Margaret. So Margaret was to meet her namesake. She was a young lady in her early twenties, and very pretty. Her lovely auburn hair was pinned up at the back of her head. She told Margaret all about her nursing training, and how she enjoyed working at the local hospital.

Her mother and Aunt Amy talked non-stop, and also commiserated with each other over the death of Margaret's father. It appeared that Aunt Amy was her father's sister.

They stayed all day. Angus talking animatedly to her cousin. Both seemed to have a lot in common. They played some records on the wind-up gramophone, which had a big brass horn on the top. Angus had to keep winding it up otherwise the record would gradually get slower and slower, which often made them laugh.

Immediately after afternoon tea they said their farewells. Aunt Amy promising to come to London to visit some time in the not too distant future.

It was late when they arrived back at the cottage. But it had been worth it, she had adored meeting nurse Margaret and her mother. Margaret had told her how she looked after people. *I would like to look after people,* she thought, though she did not feel she wanted to be a nurse, and carry bedpans, and continually make beds.

The two weeks sped by, and soon it was time to pack their things for the return journey. It had been a lovely holiday, and the only holiday that Margaret had ever known. She had spent two weeks with her mother, and felt that at last her mother cared about her. She also knew that she was not going to be left behind, though she loved Angus, he was so kind.

On the morning of their departure, Margaret hugged Aunt Clara, and her aunt wished her a safe journey, and hoped it would not be too long before they saw each other again. Angus loaded the back seat of the car with the suitcases, and once more Margaret climbed into the back seat with them. Her mother sat in the front seat next to Angus, but the mood was melancholy as they drove towards Edinburgh Railway Station.

Margaret felt positively despondent at the thought of going back to Mortlake and Ted. She had thoroughly enjoyed her two weeks in Scotland, and the attention that her mother had given her had been such a bonus.

Angus helped them onto the train, finding seats not too far from the dining car as before. William was nowhere to be seen. The big steam train was already making lots of smoke, and people were rushing to get on the train and find seats. Angus sat and talked with Margaret, as they had arrived early. He made her promise to write to him, and to answer any letters he sent to her. She promised him she would.

He put his arm round her and kissed her lightly on the cheek before making his way to the doorway, stopping to say goodbye to her mother, who had been along the corridor looking for William.

Suddenly William arrived in the doorway of the carriage. In his jolly manner, he greeted Angus. Margaret could see that her mother's face had lit up at the sight of him. Once more she felt forgotten. The big engine at the front of the train was building steam, and getting ready for the long journey. Margaret felt so sad that she was leaving Scotland, her aunt Clara who had been so kind to her, and most importantly, Angus. Yes, Angus had cared about her, and showed he genuinely liked her, she would miss him. Although he was 20 years old, he had never made her feel only ten years of age, or in any way inferior to him. He had been such good fun. The whistle went.

Angus stepped down from the train, and as the big train gently started to pull out of the station, Margaret waved furiously. Angus stood on the platform, shyly waving back. Gradually he was lost from view. How she longed to be able to come and see him again.

The train picked up speed, Margaret settled down with her book to read. It was a book Angus had given her, called *Black Beauty,* by Anna Sewell. It was not long before she was totally immersed in the story, and all too soon her mother told her it was time to go for lunch in the dining car.

They made their way along the corridor. This time they were placed at a table for four, and two other people sat there. The train was crowded, and every seat occupied. Her mother talked to William while he served them another very nice meal of soup, followed by some sort of fish, which was quite tasty. Her mother remonstrated with her for daydreaming. Margaret's mind was still linked to Edinburgh, and the good times she had had, and each mile was taking her further and further away.

The couple sitting at their table seemed very austere, and said very little to each other. Margaret wasn't sure how to react. It made her feel she had to sit very quietly, anyway. The lady was wearing a brown dress with long sleeves, but no coat or jacket, so Margaret thought it rather funny that she wore a hat on her head, also in brown, which was made of felt and had a huge brown mottled feather standing up from the crown. Every time the lady lowered her head to eat something the feather went toward the man sitting opposite her. It narrowly missed his nose once. He, on the other hand, was formally dressed in a dark suit, but wore no hat.

Once when Margaret accidentally knocked some food onto the table from her plate, the woman with the hat glowered at her. Her mother hadn't noticed, she was too busy watching William.

They returned to their seats in the carriage, and the journey continued. There were two soldiers in the carriage playing cards together, and another lady about her mother's age, and two men who appeared to be quite separate, one reading a book, and the other just looking about all the time. As he sat by the window he was often just staring outside.

They finally left the train as evening approached, and took the tube across London, eventually joining the District Line to go to Mortlake. Her mother struggled with the bigger of the two cases, and Margaret carried the small tatty one. She told her mother that Angus was going to write to her, but her mother appeared very non-committal about it. Still she hadn't told her she couldn't write back to him.

That night she was back in her own bed, which was nice. The little bed in the cottage had been all right, but it had lacked privacy, with only a curtain between her and everyone else. It had been difficult to get to sleep some nights with the adults chatting, and sometimes the wireless was on. The grown-ups had continued talking until quite late some evenings, and even if she had got off to sleep, she was sometimes woken up.

No one met them at the station, and they had to take a bus to the end of their road. Ted was at home, and greeted them both warmly. Margaret took her case up to her room, put Mr Growler on her bed, and sank down exhausted. She could hear her mother talking to Ted downstairs, and after a little while she heard the sound of crockery being put out onto the table. She was called down to have tea.

Ted asked her if she had enjoyed her trip.

'I thought it was lovely, and I thought Aunt Clara was a very nice lady,' she replied. She wasn't going to talk to him about Angus.

She did not see John until the following evening, when she told him all about her trip to Scotland. She had looked forward to telling him all that had happened, from getting on the train, to who she had seen and all the things she had done. She had been disappointed that he had not been home the evening of her return. She wondered where he kept going.

He listened attentively for some little while, and then explained to her that he had to go out as he was meeting Elsa at 8 o'clock. Her heart dropped. So that was where he had been the night before. Couldn't he see that she needed him to be with her just now?

After he left she went up to her bedroom and talked to her dolls, Jane and Megan, who both listened carefully to what she had to tell them, and afterwards she felt better.

So the school summer holidays came to a close. So much had happened in the space of a few weeks. She had finally returned from Wales to her family. She had been even further, to Scotland, on a wonderful holiday, and now she was to start school. She felt overwhelmed.

*

On the 4th September she started at the local school. Mortlake Primary was just round the corner, and she enjoyed the fact that she would start to make some friends.

Her mother took her on the first day. It only took her a few days to get to know Mrs Jolly, who was her teacher. Of all the teachers Margaret had had, Mrs Jolly was the nicest. The teacher discovered quite soon that the child worked well and was polite and helpful. Margaret soon became a classroom monitor, which entailed putting out the inkwells, as well as filling them and taking the register back to the school office. A very important position. Unfortunately there were some members of her class who were jealous of her good relationship with Mrs Jolly, and called her a "goody-goody", and other names. It reminded Margaret of the taunts she had received from Elizabeth Jones in North Wales.

She passed her termly examinations with flying colours, and learnt that the following year she would take the 11+ exams. Mrs Jolly had told her that the examinations were coming up, and that you had to pass them if you wanted to go to grammar school, or go on to college.

She thought, *If I work hard, and pass my exams I can go to Grammar School.* She had always admired the fact that her brother John had gone on to college and she dearly wanted to do this. She knew that if she wanted to be a Welfare Officer like Mr Green, she would have to study hard and pass the tests. Mrs Jolly, who knew of Margaret's ambition, had sat and told her how important it was that she was good at English and History, as well as the need to study Sociology, as that was in the curriculum of the Grammar School. She had everything to work for.

Having started private lessons in music and dancing, she had no spare time, fortunately, to have to sit in the little back room at The Royal Hotel. This was a blessing. How she hated that room.

Being good at physical education at school, and enjoying netball and rounders, put her in good stead to learn how to dance. She loved the little pink leather ballet shoes, and the little tutu she had to wear. She felt so important when she went on the bus to her dancing classes. People would look at her carrying the little pink ballet shoes. Miss Joy, her ballet teacher, taught the small class of children the finer points of delicately pointing their toes, and balancing holding the bar, some interesting steps. Margaret always saved her small amount of pocket money, to enable her to go with the other pupils into the milk bar downstairs and purchase a milkshake or a beaker of Horlicks. She longed to be able to try one of the Knickerbockers Glory ice creams, which some people ordered. One day she would order one, but she would have to save up, they were 9d.

After school on Mondays Miss Shilton, her music teacher, would come to the house. She was a jolly lady, who was rather plump. She had a kindly face and smiled all the time. She always asked Margaret to do things, rather than telling her, and Margaret appreciated this. She stayed for half an hour, which seemed to go so quickly.

Each day she was expected to practice what she had learnt each Monday. She didn't mind, she quite liked being allowed to go into the sitting room to play the piano. No one went into the sitting room, unless they had visitors. It always smelt of polish. Through the front window she could see the people passing the house. She loved watching people and how they behaved, it fascinated her.

Although her life was now quite busy, she missed the companionship she had envisaged she would have with her brother John. He was always working. Each morning early he left for London, and when he returned he either worked at the Royal Hotel in the lounge bar as a waiter, to earn extra money, or as she had discovered had started to be too friendly with the girl called Elsa. Elsa lived in Mortlake too, near the Watneys' Brewery. At weekends her brother was always missing, so she saw very little of him.

At school Margaret became friendly with a girl called Pat. Pat was an only child, and she lived in a block of flats, not far from the school, with her parents. Margaret liked Pat, but more importantly, Pat liked Margaret. They became inseparable both at school and any time Margaret was free. Pat was very lonely and encouraged Margaret to get into mischief, rather like Betty had in Wrexham. Pat was often told off at school by Mrs Jolly, because of her attention-seeking behaviour.

Sometimes when Margaret went round to the flat where Pat lived she would tell Pat she had to be home by a certain time. Pat used to encourage her to stay late, and therefore she got into trouble from her mother.

Pat's mother worked each day during the week, and did not come home until 6 o'clock. Likewise, Margaret's mother did not return home from the Royal Hotel until at least 6 o'clock. Although Margaret had to ensure that her mother's instructions were carried out, i.e. lay the table for dinner, as well as practise her piano lessons, occasionally she had to go to the bakers for a penny-three-farthing loaf, or collect some meat from the butcher. Once done her time was her own, as long as she was home when her mother arrived.

Sometimes she went straight from school to Pat's flat, and the two girls spent a lot of time together, often giggling about events of the day, and other children at school. Sometimes Margaret spent some time teaching Pat about a topic she could not understand, that Miss Jolly had been teaching them that day. Pat wasn't overly bright, and often did not understand things.

Pat's favourite pastime was to encourage Margaret to dress up in her mother's clothes and use the make-up on the dressing table. One day one of the dresses accidentally became torn, and they quickly hung it back in the wardrobe, near the back. Pat was worried what her mother would say, but this did not stop her from thinking up wonderfully mischievous ideas, some of which Margaret went along with, and others she was adamant she would not.

One day Margaret was sitting at her desk in class, when the head teacher came into the classroom and asked if anyone had any money in their desks. Margaret sat still, she knew she didn't have any. No one appeared to own up to having any. The headmistress Miss Travers, a very portly lady, then asked each child in turn to lift their desk lid as she passed along the rows of desks. When she got to Margaret, she smiled and Margaret dutifully lifted the lid. Margaret stared, she couldn't believe it, lo and behold, there was a little purse inside, and when Miss Travers lifted the purse out of the desk, there were some coins inside it. Margaret felt a guilty lump in her throat. 'It's not mine Miss,' Margaret cried.

Miss Travers looked at Margaret, the smile leaving her face, and she said, 'You had better come with me to the office.' Margaret got up and followed her. All the other children in the class were staring at her. Gosh, this felt like when she had been at All Saints School in North Wales. *How did that purse come to be in my desk?* she asked herself.

Miss Travers made her stand in front of her desk, and quietly asked her where she had acquired the purse from. Fear clutched at her heart. She started shaking. 'I don't know anything about it,' Margaret replied. 'It wasn't there earlier this morning Miss Travers.'

She was questioned over and over again, but her story never changed. She was made to sit outside the head's office. A little while later she saw that her mother had arrived at the school, and was taken into Miss Travers' office. *Oh Lord, whatever next?* she thought. *Where could that purse have come from?*

A little while later, she herself was called back into the head teacher's office. Her mother sat the other side of the desk, where she herself had sat earlier. Her mother looked stern and unsmiling.

Her mother asked, 'Where did you get the purse Miss Travers found in your desk? It isn't mine.'

The child started to cry. Through her tears she said, 'I don't know, it was just in my desk, someone must have put it there'. The questioning went on.

It was some while later that she was allowed to go back to her class. She had taken herself to the cloakroom first to wash her face, which was by then all blotchy and red.

Everyone looked up when she entered the classroom. She sat down at her desk feeling very embarrassed. Miss Jolly told her the book they were reading, and she lifted her desk lid and put the book on the desk top. She sat with her head bent for the rest of the lesson.

At break time Pat came over and asked how she had got on. Margaret told her how bad she felt, but that she didn't know how she came to have a purse in her desk. The purse had contained £2, a lot of money.

Pat said, 'Don't' say anything will you, but I took that purse from my mother's bag last night.'

Margaret stared at her friend. 'Why did you do that?' she asked.

'Because I hate my mother,' she replied, 'she said I couldn't go to dancing classes like you, she said she couldn't afford it, so I took the money. If I can't go to dancing classes, I thought, I would spend some of the money on what I wanted to.'

Margaret was stunned. 'But you have got me into trouble, why did you put it in my desk?' she asked.

'Well, I knew they wouldn't suspect you, I didn't know they would look in everyone's desk like they did. If my mother had missed it and come to the school I thought they would only look in my desk, or in my coat,' Pat told her.

Margaret groaned. Her best friend had got her into trouble, and now if she split on her Pat would get into trouble also. She just couldn't do it. She felt sorry for Pat, who had such a lonely life and was so unhappy. No, she couldn't let her friend get into trouble. If she said nothing, it would look as if she herself had taken the purse after school yesterday when she was at her friend's flat. What was she to do? If only she could talk to John.

The rest of the day Margaret crept about the school, trying to look inconspicuous. Mrs Jolly, her teacher, was her normal self and talked to Margaret as if nothing had happened earlier in the day.

Her mother had disappeared. Margaret had a sudden thought. Her mother went to work this morning. Had the school asked her to come all the way from Richmond, and was she home now? It was during the second lesson in the afternoon that she realised that Pat was not at her desk. Where could she be?

Home time came and still no Pat. She picked up her school bag and went straight home. Her mother was waiting for her in the kitchen.

Her mother glared at her, 'Fancy my having to be called to the school this morning young lady. I felt so ashamed, to think you had taken some money, after all we provide for you.'

'But I didn't take any money,' Margaret cried.

Her mother ignored her. 'I was so humiliated being spoken to by the headmistress,' her mother raved. 'I spent nearly all day at the school.'

'No, you didn't take the money, that no good friend of yours did. Miss Travers had her in her office this afternoon, and in the end she confessed. You keep away from that girl, she is trouble,' her mother went on.

'But she is my friend, and she didn't mean to take the money, it was her mother who had kept her short of money.'

Suddenly she realised she had let the cat out of the bag. Her mother said, 'I knew it, she's a bad lot, don't ever let me see you with her again, do you hear me?' Margaret just nodded.

But she liked Pat, they were good friends. No one played with her, she would be so lonely. Margaret ran upstairs to her room. Was she never to have any friends to talk to, no friend of her own?

There was no Mrs Perie, No Mr Green, No Bobbie, No Patch, and quite often no John. She had no idea when she would see Angus again, and now no Pat.

She felt so lonely.

Chapter 13

That evening she sat on the veranda steps feeling miserable, when John appeared. He came up the steps from the garden and sat beside her.

'What's up sis?' he asked.

She told him about the happenings at the school that day, and then about her mother's wrath when she had returned home.

'I thought she was in a strop,' he replied, 'she was very off hand with me too.'

'What am I to do John?' she asked him, 'I like Pat, she is my friend, but if I see her or talk to her Mummy will be cross.'

'Margaret, Pat has got you into trouble before, even though it was only for minor things; she is very mischievous, I don't think you should continue to have her as your friend. I know it is hard, but if you aggravate mother she will possibly stop you playing the piano, or worse. She is bound to punish you in some way. You are doing so well, it costs a lot of money to have private lessons.' Quietly he added, 'She may even send you away again.'

Margaret froze. Oh no, she didn't want to be sent away again. She also liked playing the piano. Miss Shilton, her music teacher, was such a nice lady, and she knew what John said was true, she was doing well, and could play small pieces of music, and soon Miss Shilton had indicated that she could be put forward for her first exam. Also, if she didn't have music lessons on Monday afternoons, she might have to go to the hotel until her mother finished work. On Mondays her mother worked until half past seven. The thought of the little back room was enough to deter her.

Sadly, she knew that she had no choice. She would not be able to talk with Pat again, nor play with her after school.

She knew John was right, and was glad that he had made her see sense. She loved John, he was so sensible.

John went on to tell Margaret that he had just had a row with his girlfriend Elsa. Margaret suddenly felt elated. Perhaps he wouldn't see her any more and John would be at home more often so that she could talk with him.

John was telling her that the row had been so stupid. Elsa had wanted him to take time off work to go somewhere, but he had decided he could not afford to do this. They had argued for some time, but he had been adamant. Margaret was well aware that her brother was very stubborn, and if he made up his mind about something, he would not budge.

They sat there for some time in companionable silence, listening to the birds twittering, both deep in thought. Ten minutes passed, when John suddenly said, 'Could you run an errand for me sis?

'What sort of errand?' she asked him.

She remembered errands she had run for Mrs Hall. She also didn't want to antagonise her mother by being missing too long.

'Just take a note to Elsa's house for me, it is only just past the school, opposite the brewery, and wait and get a reply, would you?'

Well, that seemed reasonable. She would do anything for John. She had completed all her chores, her mother wouldn't mind her just going by the school.

'Yes, all right, I'll go for you.'

John went off into the house, while she continued to sit and think about what he had said about Pat. She would have to find another friend. She couldn't think of anyone else that she really liked at school. She had enjoyed going with Pat after school each day. She had been such fun to be with. But she knew John was right, he was always right. Unfortunately she would have to find a new friend.

Some little while later, John appeared with a letter, which she tucked inside the elastic of her navy blue school knickers. She went down the steps of the veranda and out of the back gate. She walked along beside the railway lines, until she could join the road which went past the school. Some little way past she came to the Jolly Milkman pub, where John had told her to turn right into Croft Lane. She walked quickly until she came to the tall houses on the right hand side of the road, and noted the first one was No 5. This must be Elsa's house, she decided.

She climbed the half a dozen stone steps up to the front door. There were lots of empty milk bottles placed on the side of the top step. *They must use a lot of milk,* she thought. She rapped the knocker and waited. The door was soon opened by a little middle-aged lady. She had a small face, with a rather beaky nose, and dark hair. She was wearing a coloured overall which almost covered her dress.

'What is it you want?' she enquired.

Margaret soon told her that she had a letter which she had to give to Elsa personally. The woman looked her over quickly then ushered her through the doorway, and asked her to follow her upstairs. It was rather dark and dingy in the hallway, and the light above the stairs was very dim. They climbed a whole flight of stairs almost in the dark, and arrived in front of a door, which they entered.

This must be Elsa's mother, Margaret thought. As she followed the woman into the large living room, she noted it smelt very warm and homely, and there were lots of plates still on the large table, as though everyone had just finished eating. There were at least five people in the room. A tall man, who she learnt was Elsa's father, was just seating himself in the chair next to the range. A boy not much older than herself, and two other girls were deep in conversation on the far side of the room, and then there was the lady who had brought her up.

'Sit down dear, make yourself at home, Elsa is upstairs having a wash momentarily, she has only just come in from work, she won't be long.'

Margaret found an empty chair and sat down. What an unusual house, the living room was upstairs! The table was very big and had lots of wooden chairs round it. The boy moved away from the girls, who were still busy chattering away, but at the same time kept looking at her, obviously quite curious to know what she was doing there. Elsa's mother came and went every so often, and eventually started to clear plates from the table.

It was stifling hot in the room, even though one of the windows was open a bit. No one seemed to notice. Margaret felt very self-conscious, and wished Elsa would hurry up so that she could get back home.

The next minute Mrs Barnes was offering her a glass of lemon squash, which she gratefully accepted. She sipped the cool liquid and started to feel better, she hadn't realised how thirsty she was.

She had almost finished her drink when a girl in her late teens came into the room. She was very pretty, with dark hair and brown eyes, wearing a flowery blue and pink dress. She smiled at Margaret and said, 'My mother tells me you have a letter for me.' So this must be Elsa, no wonder her brother liked her, she was really lovely. She put the glass down on the table and quickly pulled out the letter from its hiding place in her knickers.

She watched Elsa read the letter and then smile. Elsa turned and went over to the sideboard, and opening one of the top drawers she took out some paper, and sat at the table and started to write. After some minutes she folded the paper, put it in an envelope, and stood up. She held out the envelope to Margaret.

'Please would you be so kind as to take this letter back to John, and be sure that only John reads it.'

Margaret stood up, took the letter from her, and retraced her steps out of the house. Outside, she once more tucked the letter into her knickers.

She hurried home and ran upstairs to find John in his bedroom. She gave him the note and stood watching him. He suddenly brightened, and he smiled at her. 'Thanks sis,' was all he said. She hadn't been able to read the letters, but dearly wished to know what they contained. Elsa had appeared happy, and John had certainly seemed pleased after reading the reply. She returned to her own bedroom and started getting her things ready for school the next day.

*

No one at school said anything further about the money. Pat was back at her desk, and tried whispering to Margaret, but she was not to be swayed. Although she felt sorry for Pat, she knew she could not defy her mother. It was some days before Pat seemed to get the message and stopped troubling her.

Margaret made herself useful in the classroom, and stayed behind to help Mrs Jolly clear up. Another girl also seemed to stay behind and help, her name was Valerie. They appeared to get on so well that Margaret wondered why she had never been friends with her before. Their friendship grew over the next few days, but was very much confined to the school, as after school Valerie had to go home in the opposite direction, and collect her small brother from the infants' school on the way.

Valerie was not what you would call a pretty girl, but she had a lovely smile, and what Margaret liked best about her was that she listened attentively to you when you spoke to her. The only thing that no one ever considered doing was listening to how she felt about things. Mrs Jolly listened but always appeared busy with other things at the same time, and John only listened occasionally when he was about. Sometimes he chided her, and told her she was silly. Valerie wasn't like either of them, which was so refreshing.

She had lovely long blonde hair, which fell softly over her shoulders, her face was sparingly covered in freckles, which became more prominent when the weather was hot, or the room they were in was hot and stuffy, as well as when she blushed, which she did quite often. Mrs Jolly liked Valerie, because the girl took a lot of trouble with her school work, and she was always willing to help Mr Jolly by putting books out or cleaning the blackboard for her after lessons. So Margaret once more came into favour.

Some two weeks after their friendship began, Margaret was invited to Valerie's house for her birthday tea. No other child had been invited, so she felt honoured. She found the house quite easily, although it was a mile past the school. It was a terraced house, with pretty curtains at the windows. She opened the gate and walked up the path, carefully carrying the parcel containing the autograph book she had bought as a present. She was wearing the pretty dress that Ted had bought for her some weeks ago. Her mother only let her wear it for special occasions.

Valerie was sitting inside the front window and saw her approaching the front door, and quickly ran round to open it for her. Margaret handed her the little parcel, which Valerie thanked her for most profusely. She was so excited, and once opened she ran into the sitting room to show it to her mother. She turned and said, 'Thank you so much Margaret, it is just what I have always wanted.'

Her mother was a kindly lady, who made Margaret feel very welcome. Valerie's little brother, who was only 6 years of age, followed them everywhere. Like Valerie, he had lots of freckles on his face. Unlike her, he had ginger hair, and Margaret soon learned that Joey rarely did as he was told. But Mrs Stacey didn't seem to mind, and obviously doted on both her two children. She had made a beautiful birthday cake for her daughter with ten candles on the top. There had been dainty little sandwiches and small little cakes with papers round the outside, and coloured icing on the tops. Then there were little jellies in paper dishes in the shape of flowers. Mrs Stacey also brought in a junket, and a blancmange, Ooh, what a treat!

It was her own birthday next week. She decided she would ask her mother if Valerie could come to tea.

Joey was told more than once to sit still or he would not have any jelly or cake, but he just could not keep still, and after eating his jelly he got down and started playing with his toy car. No one took any real notice, so Margaret went on eating. When the candles on the cake were lit, he did, however, come over and watch his sister blow out the candles.

All too soon it was time to go home. She had so enjoyed her afternoon, and was pleased when Mrs Stacey said she would have to come again some time, saying it was nice for Valerie to have a friend.

She skipped home most of the way, quite happy. When she arrived at her own house her mother was in the kitchen ironing. She asked Margaret if she had enjoyed herself.

'We had a lovely tea, and Valerie blew out the ten candles on the top of the cake. Mrs Stacey is very nice, and has suggested I could go again some time.'

'Well, if you are good, you may be able to. Valerie appears to be a nice girl,' her mother said.

'It will be my birthday next week, could I have Valerie to tea?' Margaret asked.

'Oh, I don't know about that, we'll have to wait and see,' her mother replied.

Well, she hadn't said no, best to wait and see. She ran upstairs to her room still feeling so happy. Yes, Valerie was a nicer girl than Pat, though she missed Pat. Valerie wasn't as much fun.

Later that evening she listened to the little wireless in the dining room. The broadcaster was reading the news. The British troops had landed in Singapore, and the Japanese forces in South East Asia had surrendered to Lord Mountbatten. It seemed to Margaret that all sorts of countries were at war. The war with Germany had ended earlier that year, and now another war involving the British Troops was hopefully over in the Far East. Her mother had been intent on listening to the news of late, and her brother Robbie was aboard a ship out in the Far East. He was now a Petty Officer on some ship. So many boats were being sunk, her mother worried about him. She was forever saying, 'Whenever will these wars be over?'

Three days went by, and her mother never mentioned anything about her birthday, so she plucked up courage to ask again. She waited until her mother was settled after the evening meal and had picked up her knitting.

'Mummy, have you decided if I can have Valerie to tea on Saturday?'

Her mother looked up. 'I'm afraid I have to work on Saturday, so I won't be able to make a special tea for your birthday, perhaps your friend can come some other time when I'm not so busy.' Her mother went on, 'I'm knitting you a jumper for your birthday, but as you can see I haven't finished the second sleeve yet, so you won't be able to wear it until next week at the earliest, but it will keep you warm during the winter.'

Margaret's heart sank, no birthday tea, and she had implied to Valerie at school that she would be coming.

'Couldn't I have a birthday tea on Sunday instead?' she asked.

'I'm, afraid not, Ted wants me to meet someone he knows on Sunday afternoon.'

Margaret ran upstairs, so terribly upset. How was she going to tell Valerie that she wasn't coming to tea on Saturday, and her birthday present was to be that jumper her mother was knitting. She had helped her mother unravel one of the boy's jumpers and wind the wool some weeks ago. She had wound the skeins which had been placed into the steamer to smooth out all the crinkles. She had been looking forward to something nice.

Her birthday came and went, just like any other ordinary day. How embarrassed she had been to tell Valerie that she was not having a birthday tea. Valerie had however, bought her a box of Bassett's Liquorice Allsorts, which she loved.

John had already asked her what she would like, and had given her a whole five shillings to purchase some material, as she wanted to make a dress for herself. She had been learning to sew at school, and her teacher said she could borrow one of the school patterns if she wanted to attempt to make something at home. So the following Saturday she had been allowed to take the bus into Richmond and buy the material from the haberdashery shop. She bought three yards of green and white gingham, and two reels of cotton. Her mother had an old Singer sewing machine. She returned home with her treasures and set about cutting out the pattern pieces ready to assemble. Although her teacher had encouraged her in her sewing she had learnt most of her sewing skills from Mrs Perie, as well as some hidden knowledge of her own. She was later to learn that her grandmother had been a seamstress, and very clever with her needle.

She had more time on her hands after school now that she did not have Pat to hang around with, and within two weeks the dress was complete. How proud she was of her achievement. Her mother actually seemed impressed with the garment, and with her ability at sewing. However, her mother soon found her some sewing tasks to do; patching sheets, putting sides to middles; mending blouses, and sewing on buttons which had come off shirts.

Ted and her mother worked right through Christmas which was a busy time in the hotel, so Christmas passed by without any of the enjoyment she had been looking forward to. Her mother also said that money was scarce, and they shouldn't waste money unnecessarily.

Her first visit to Elsa's house soon became quite a regular occurrence. Not that John sent her often with messages, but her mother sent messages to John to come home, as he spent most of his time at Croft Lane when he wasn't working. She was quite a regular visitor there, and she knew all the family quite well.

*

Early in 1946 her mother told her that she was to be a bridesmaid, as her eldest brother, William, was getting married to Ellen. She also learnt that the wedding was to be held in Rhyl, in North Wales, where his fiancé lived with her parents. How was her mother going to afford the fare for them to go? She had only been able to visit North Wales once and see her whilst she had been evacuated. Her mother was always moaning she had little money. However, there was much excitement. Margaret had long since come to understand that her mother thought the world of William, and would do anything for him.

She could recall when she had been six years old, and her brother had come home on leave from the Royal Air Force, that her mother had dashed around buying and acquiring food she could ill afford, or get; and the fact that her mother had given up her own bed for William, and she had shared Margaret's bed. She remembered it so well, because her mother had brought in a loud alarm clock, which had ticked away all night, and she had been unable to sleep.

It was April when they had travelled on the train to Rhyl. Ellen was to be married at the local church. Her mother told her that there was to be another bridesmaid, who was much older than Margaret.

When she saw the dress she was to wear, she was thrilled and excited. This was going to be fun. The dress was made of pale blue satin, and it came right down to her feet. She had never worn a long dress before. Ellen's mother had made some little bands of pink and blue flowers to wear in their hair. She was to have her hair tonged into ringlets.

They had arrived in Rhyl some three days before the wedding, and Ellen, who seemed very nice, took Margaret shopping and purchased a pair of white satin shoes, and little white lace gloves to match.

One fly in the ointment had been that Ted had come as well. What with her mother doting on William, and attempting to impress Ellen's mother and father, any spare time she had was taken up with Ted. Margaret felt very isolated, but joined in many of the activities. The night before the wedding lots of women were busy making sandwiches and sausage rolls in the kitchen, though she had been told to keep out of the way. Ellen's mother, although very busy, came and found her sitting quietly in the sitting room.

'Come along Margaret, I have just the job for you,' she said. Margaret followed her down the corridor, across the hallway, and into a small room, which had a desk in it and books on the shelves. A large Captain's chair was in front of the desk. 'Sit here dear, and I'll show you what needs to be done.' Mrs Miles opened a drawer, extracted some coloured sheets of paper, and a small machine.

'Just hold this paper punch in one hand, and the paper in the other, and when you press you will see that lots of little bits of paper fall into the bottom of the machine. These we will use for confetti. Do you think you could do that for me?' she asked.

'Yes, Mrs Mills, I think I could do that.'

She was left alone, and within half an hour she had made piles of little circles. She put them all into the bags that Mrs Mills had left her.

Her mother came and found her, and told her she must be very good, and not do anything silly or she would be cross. Her mother was quite specific, all she had to do was follow Ellen wherever she went. *Well, that should be easy enough to do,* she thought.

The big day dawned. Everyone was rushing round when she came down for breakfast, which had been laid out in the dining room so that you could help yourself. She chose some cornflakes, pouring a generous portion of milk over them, and sugar, and afterwards helping herself to two pieces of toast. There was some lovely honey on the table, which she had first had when she visited Scotland last year. Mmm, it tasted good.

Her mother insisted she had another bath, before putting on the long blue dress. One of Ellen's Aunties washed her hair, and when it was nearly dry, tonged it into ringlets.

162

Gosh, didn't she look different!

Her mother took her up to Ellen's bedroom, where she was introduced to Jilly, who was the other bridesmaid. She had only just arrived back from her unit. Both Ellen and Jilly had been in the WAAFs together, and were good friends.

Everyone helped them into the dresses. Margaret preened herself in front of the long cheval mirror. Ellen looked so elegant in her long white dress. Carefully the headdress was clipped into her hair, behind which trailed lots of tulle. Her mother said, 'Margaret, you will be walking directly behind Ellen, and you must carry the back of the train like this.' She watched what her mother was showing her to do.

'All right, I will hold the train as well as the end of the veil all the time,' she said. No one told her that when Ellen went further up the aisle to the altar with William for the blessing, that she should have stayed where she was.

The two bridesmaids went first, and Ellen and her father went in the car behind. They stood aside while Ellen walked through the door of the big church, and then Margaret followed, after picking up the train and veil as she had been schooled to do, then Jilly took up the rear. The little procession made its way slowly up the aisle to the strains of *"Here Comes the Bride"*.

All seemed well. She held the train tightly. After the vows had been taken, and the congregation stood and started singing the final hymn, Ellen started to move forward with William to mount the steps leading up the altar. Someone saw Margaret starting to move and told her to stay where she was. Oh, what should she do? She was still holding the train and veil tightly, too tightly. Ellen took another step forward, and the headdress started to come off her head.

Fortunately Ellen stood still realising what was happening, and turned to Margaret:

'I have to go on my own with William,' she whispered.

Margaret dropped the veil and stood still. She then realised that Ellen's headdress was tilted at an angle, and looked as though it would fall off.

It was a beautiful wedding, and William looked very smart in his Air Force Uniform. Apart from the wonky headdress Ellen had looked beautiful in her lovely satin wedding dress.

Photographs were taken outside the church, before they once more went into the cars waiting at the kerb, and were whisked off to the reception, which was being held nearby in a small hotel. Margaret tucked into the sandwiches, and watched while Ellen and William cut the tiered wedding cake.

Much later, back at the house, her mother sought her out, and demanded to know why she had not done as she was told. She ranted and raved at Margaret, and suggested that the child had nearly ruined her brother's wedding. Could she do nothing right? It appeared that her mother did not think so.

The following day, and all too soon, they started to make their way home. Margaret would have liked to go into the town and find the milk bar that Pamela Perie had taken her to. But her mother would not hear of it. 'I have to get back to work, and so does Ted. The train leaves in two hours, so there is no time. Come along, hurry up and get your things together.'

* * *

Chapter 14

The train journey home was not a very enjoyable experience. Her mother hadn't fully forgiven her for the indiscretion with the headdress, and therefore was not prepared to talk nicely with her. Most of the journey her mother talked to Ted, complaining bitterly about all and everything. Mr and Mrs Miles hadn't impressed her that much, and it became obvious that her mother was jealous of their assets.

'That girl Ellen is not good enough for my son,' she went on, 'mind you, he only met her in the Air Force, if things had been normal he would have found someone much better.'

'I am really cross and upset that my William is going to live up here in North Wales, when will I ever get to see him?' she bemoaned her lot continually.

Ted remained calm as he usually did, and tried to get her mother to look at the advantages of each situation she presented. Margaret stared out of the train window, and was pleased when at last they arrived at Euston Station. She loved London, and as they made their way across the city Margaret once again marvelled at the lovely buildings. They crossed Westminster Bridge on the bus, and eventually arrived at Waterloo, where they once more boarded a train to take them back to Richmond.

*

On returning to school after the Easter break, she was told that the following week she would be sitting her 11+ examinations.

Gosh, it was so important for her to pass. She needed to go to Grammar School. Margaret never shared her aspirations with her mother, who never seemed to listen properly when she tried to talk to her. John listened to her when he was about, but this was rare these days. He did though, encourage her to try hard and pass her exams.

The first exam was mathematics, not her favourite subject. She was very nervous, but once she had settled down, she realised that the questions were just like those from her recent lessons. The following day she took the English paper and had to write a short piece about a prescribed topic, "A Birthday Cake". The only cake she had ever had for her birthday was the one Mrs Perie had made for her, so she wrote about that. Then there were pieces of written text in which she had to put in punctuation marks, and re-write in the third person. That seemed easy enough too. Her teacher had told her that the questions might be hard, or she might not understand them. But she did.

Some weeks went by before Mrs Holly, her teacher, told the class that the results of the 11+ were in, and that if she called out someone's name they were to go into the school hall straight away. Three or four names were called out, and then Margaret heard her own name. She rose and walked out of the classroom and into the school hall. It was as though her feet had wings, and her heart felt so light. She had passed!

There were a few chairs placed in a circle near to the platform. She was told to sit on one. Each child was handed a sheet of paper, and Miss Travers, the headmistress, who was standing on the raised platform, told them that they must take the invitations home to their parents. She confirmed they had each passed their 11+ exams and that their parents would come to the school next week for interviews with their child. Margaret was so excited. She had done it, she could go to the Grammar School!

She skipped all the way home from school, clutching the prized invitation for her mother to attend the school the following week. Alas, her mother was not at home when she arrived. She busied herself, laying the table for dinner, and cleaning her shoes for the next day.

When her mother arrived Margaret couldn't stop talking.

'Stop it, slow down!' her mother shouted, 'I can't tell a word you are saying, child.'

'I've passed my 11+ exams,' Margaret explained, 'you have to go to the school next week for the interviews. I can go to the Grammar School.'

'I don't know about that,' her mother took off her coat and hung it on the hallstand. 'It will cost a lot of money, and the uniform is expensive for a start.'

Margaret looked despondent. 'But I need to go to Grammar School so that I can go to College.' Surely her mother could understand.

Reluctantly her mother agreed to go to the interview the following Wednesday. It would be all right, her teacher would tell her mother she must go. At least her mother was going to the interview. She flew upstairs, feeling ecstatic.

The days ticked slowly by. Margaret did well with her music teacher, who was pleased the child had practised so well. She was also doing well at dancing school, and had learnt this week that the dancing school was putting on a production at the Kingston Empire in two months time, and that she would need a proper ballet dress called a tutu, as well as an outfit for her tap dancing routine. She was to have a spot of her own, as well as doing a duet with another girl. They were to sing the new hit song, *"A, You're Adorable"* together.

Her mother was not pleased about the expense of the costumes necessary for her to take part in the production.

However, Margaret overheard Ted say to her mother, 'If the child needs these things, get them, I will pay for them.'

She wasn't happy that he would be paying for them, but as she was in good spirits at present, and she needed the costumes so badly she elected to accept without causing any fuss. She hated Ted paying for things for her, he wasn't her father.

The following Wednesday Margaret arrived at school early. She was very agitated and nervous, but at 2 o'clock the parents started to arrive, her mother among them. Each parent was seen by the headmistress in her office. Margaret was told to follow her mother in. Miss Travers shook her mother's hand, and congratulated her that her daughter had passed the examinations, and that the English paper had been passed with honours.

Margaret preened, she had done well.

Miss Travers explained that if Margaret went to the Grammar School, her mother had to agree to her staying on until she was 18 years of age. Margaret stared at her mother, she was shaking her head.

Miss Travers went on to explain about uniforms, and other expenses, such as hockey sticks and tennis racquets. The Grammar School was in Richmond, and only children who attended the Secondary school had bus fares paid by the Education Department.

Margaret listened with horror as she heard her mother say, 'I can't afford for Margaret to stay at school until she is eighteen. The uniform is expensive as well, as I would have to provide her with sports equipment of her own, no, I could not afford that. I do not believe in girls going to College later on as you have indicated. If Margaret had been a boy things might be different. No, I am sorry, I can't let Margaret go to the Grammar School.'

'Oh Mummy please,' Margaret pleaded, 'I must go to the Grammar School, I want to be a Welfare Officer when I leave school, oh please.'

But her mother was adamant. No amount of pleading seemed to change her mind. There was to be no Grammar School, her hopes were dashed, she was desolate. She was told to return to her class. How horrid her mother was. She had worked so hard, and now she couldn't go. She would rather have gone to the Grammar School than all her dancing classes. Couldn't her mother understand she *had to* go! She neither heard nor saw anything for the rest of the afternoon. She just sat, stunned.

When school broke up for the day, she dragged herself home and went straight upstairs to her room. She had such mixed emotions of anger, sadness, and humiliation. She had worked so hard, and for what? She couldn't go to the Grammar School. How she hated her mother.

Her mother had shown she had not wanted her to come home from North Wales. She had only visited her the once in three whole years, she couldn't have missed her. She hadn't wanted Margaret to keep little Patch, who she still missed so terribly, and now she didn't want her to go to St Hilda's. How would she learn Sociology? Mrs Jolly had said quite clearly that St Hilda's was where she would learn it, not at the local Secondary School.

She decided she could not go downstairs and face her mother. She should be laying the table for dinner, but she decided she couldn't go. Hot tears flowed down her cheeks, her throat felt constricted. She threw herself on the bed and sobbed. She had no idea how long she had been there, nor was she aware that her mother had popped her head round the door, and on seeing the distress her daughter was in decided to leave her to cry it out. After all there was no way she could let her daughter go to the Grammar School, there simply wasn't the money, especially now they had the house, and Margaret was already having private lessons for music and dancing, which Ted was paying for. No, she couldn't ask Ted to finance anything else. The child would get over it. The High School was just as good, and they supplied most of the things Margaret would need. She could just about manage to buy a basic uniform.

When Margaret eventually emerged from her bedroom later that evening, the house was quiet, and it was dark. She crept downstairs and into the kitchen. The table was empty. Where was everyone? She looked in all the rooms, but no one was at home except herself. She went back into the kitchen, and in the oven she found the remains of her dinner, covered with a plate. It was warm, but very dried up. She was hungry so she sat and ate it. Afterwards she took herself to bed. She later heard people downstairs, but remained where she was, curled up into a little ball, and fell asleep.

Her mother never referred to the incident, nor talked about why she was not going to the Grammar School. Margaret felt depressed for weeks, and had no enthusiasm with her work. Mrs Jolly tried hard to cheer her up saying, 'It isn't the end of the world not going to St Hilda's; Gainsborough High School is a very good school, I'm sure you will like it there.' But nothing anyone said made any difference to Margaret's thinking. She was not going to the school she had set her heart on, and that was that.

*

School broke up in July, and this included her private lessons. The long holiday lay ahead. There were days when she had to sit in the little back room at The Royal, but her mother often made use of her to run errands, and this somehow helped. Before the bars were open to the public

Margaret would help her mother by cutting up potatoes which had been partly cooked, to make potato salad, or grate carrots and cabbage for coleslaw. Hard-boiled eggs had to be sliced, and various meats cut into thin slices. Sandwiches had to be made. She quite enjoyed doing all this. Her mother appeared grateful for her help as well.

Mr Cane, the Manager, liked Margaret, and often gave her little treats. This usually amounted to small bags of sweets, (as sweets were still on ration Margaret much appreciated this) as well as bags of fruit, which her mother always said were too expensive to buy, and were a luxury. On one occasion he bought her some crayons and a colouring book, and on another a magic colouring book, which you just painted with water, and a coloured picture emerged before your eyes.

Mr Cane had heard about her dog Patch, and unbeknown to Margaret, or to her mother, had colluded with Ted to buy her another puppy. One day he came towards Margaret with a large box. The box had holes in the side. 'Here you are Margaret, I hope you like it and will look after it,' he offered her the box.

Margaret took the box from him, gosh, it was heavy. She placed it on the floor and opened it. She stared in amazement for there, snuggled down in the straw, was a soft, cuddly little puppy. 'It's a female,' Mr Cane told her, 'it was the nearest one I could find that looked like Patch.'

'Oh, she's lovely.' She bent down and picked up the little bundle in her arms. She was beautiful, all brown and black, a sort of Yorkshire terrier. She had lovely large brown eyes, and light brown hair that fell all over her face. Margaret's heart felt full, tears sprang to her eyes, even though she felt so happy. A little dog of her own again. The puppy could never take Patch's place, but she loved her on sight. The next two hours passed so quickly in the little back room, with the puppy for company, then it was time to take it home.

Her mother's face looked thunderous, she said little to the child as they climbed onto the bus, nor during the entire journey. Considering Margaret had helped her behind the bar earlier on, she felt mortally wounded that her mother was not talking to her. As soon as they were home, and in no uncertain terms, her mother told her that the puppy was confined to the scullery and the garden. Margaret promised to ensure that would be so, and took the puppy out into the garden with her.

What could she call her? The puppy looked so funny walking around the garden. It swayed as though it was drunk, as it was rather unsteady on its legs. It came back to Margaret time and time again, and she cuddled it, loving the feel of its soft coat. She was so cute. 'I think I'll call you Peggy,' she told the puppy. She had no idea why she wanted to call her Peggy, but Peggy she became. Margaret could not understand why her mother did not like the little dog, how could anyone not love her?

It certainly helped the school holiday. She did not mind the days in the little back room at the hotel now that she had Peggy for company. As the little puppy grew, Margaret realised that there were never any rats to be seen in the little dark room whilst the dog was there. She could spend time going along the towpath of the river, taking Peggy for walks, and at home she could play in the garden with the dog, as well as take her for walks. She was good company when Margaret had to do errands to Elsa's house, or collect some shopping.

Peggy soon learnt that although she was not allowed into some parts of the house, she could run up the veranda steps, and if Margaret had the veranda doors open she could get into her bedroom and be near her. If Margaret heard her mother coming up the stairs she could put the dog outside the doors.

Her mother found a dressmaker to make the ballet dress she needed, as well as a suitable outfit for her part in the duo. She had to go regularly for fittings. It all seemed great fun, except sometimes it was very painful, as the dressmaker often stuck the pins into her skin accidentally; but Margaret was thrilled with the clothes.

The tutu had a bright red satin bodice, and the skirt was made of red tulle with tarlatan underneath, so that it splayed out. Sequins sparkled all over the skirt, and red rhinestones emphasised the top of the bodice. She was to be a jewel in the ballet, and her part was that of a ruby. Her mother bought her new red ballet shoes to match as well. The dressmaker had made a little white silk blouse, and black floppy trousers for the tap routine. An enormous silk tartan bow was attached to the neck of the blouse, and the entire ensemble looked extremely chic.

She was looking forward to the production. She had never been on the stage before, and there were now only a few weeks before the November date.

Since her return from Scotland the year before, Margaret had received three letters from Angus. The first one had arrived just after her tenth birthday. She had been ecstatic when it arrived, and she had waited until she was alone to read it. What lovely writing he had:

Dear Margaret,

I hope the journey back to London was a pleasant one, and that you have now settled in at school. The weather here in Scotland is variable; sometimes quite pleasant, but sometimes quite wild and windy. I saw cousin Margaret the other day when I called at the hospital where she works, and she sends you her love.

I seem to have a bad cold at the moment and will be pleased when it improves, to enable me to decorate Aunt Clara's cottage. There are some improvements which I need to do now before the weather makes it impossible to do.

I look forward to hearing from you. Please give my kind regards to Aunt Jane.

Signed,
Angus.

Margaret couldn't wait to find the time to sit and write a reply. She had so much to tell him about her school, and her music lessons, which she loved, together with the ballet and tap lessons at the dancing school. That week she posted off the reply. She had written reams, she knew he would understand how excited she was at present.

The second letter did not arrive until January. She had been surprised not to hear from him at Christmas, but knew he must have been busy. His second letter was shorter than the first.

Dear Margaret,

Thank you for your very nice letter. I can see you are busy learning lots of things, I am very proud of you. Keep up the good work. No doubt you will let me know how you progress.

Aunt Clara is well, please give my kind regards to Aunt Jane.

Best Wishes,
Angus.

She was pleased he had understood her letter, but his letter was so short, she felt quite some disappointment.

The following week she wrote back, giving him all the news, and intimating she had spent a rather miserable Christmas, but that her mother had been working. She had showed her mother Angus's letter, who appeared pleased he had sent his good wishes to her. 'Angus is such a nice young man, he will make someone a very good husband one day,' she remarked.

It was some months before she received his third letter, which went on to tell her he had been in hospital.

Dear Margaret

I am sorry I have not written before, but I have been incarcerated here in a sanatorium. The cold I had earlier in the year didn't improve, and I developed a nasty cough. However, they are looking after me extremely well, and I hope to go home some time soon.

Aunt Clara comes regularly to visit me, so I am sure she will deliver any letter you send.

I was glad to hear all about the proposed wedding of William. By now he will be married.

One day I hope to marry and have some children of my own, but that day is far off at present.

Give my kind regards to Aunt Jane.

Take care of yourself Margaret.

Best wishes,

Angus.

At the end of August her mother took her to buy the school uniform for when she started at Gainsborough High

School the following month. She disliked the tunic which was made of rough navy serge, and the silly felt hat, with its turned up brim, just like a St Trinians. Everything was navy blue, even her knickers, which she learnt she would wear when performing games and PE in the playground outside, where the boys would be watching from their side of the fence. The school was divided into two parts. Boys in one half and girls in the other. The segregation made you feel differently about boys. She had never noticed the difference at Mortlake C of E, they were just all children. Now they were a separate entity, she wondered why.

*

She started her new school on the 4th September 1946, just before her eleventh birthday.

She instantly liked the school. The corridors were all made of grey marble, both on the floors and two thirds up the walls. All the stairs were made of grey marble also. Classrooms were on either side of the long corridor, and the headmistress's room was at the far end. Then there was an "inner sanctum", only entered into for discipline or praise.

Margaret loved all the different rooms, and it was strange having to move to different classrooms for different lessons. The teachers stayed where they were, and every subject had a different teacher.

She soon established herself once more as a keen student. She excelled in English, Art and Needlework. She loved sport and was keen to be allowed to go swimming, she had always wanted to learn.

She told her mother she would need a swimming costume to be allowed to go. Her mother, as usual, stated the obvious. There were no clothing coupons to buy one, also no money to spare. It was some days after she had mentioned it that she learnt her mother was going to knit her one. Mrs Trent was unravelling a pea green woollen jumper.

'What are you doing Mummy?' Margaret asked.

'I'm going to unpick this jumper and knit you a swimming costume so that you can go swimming, as I think you should learn,' she told the child.

'Great,' she thought, 'I have always wanted to learn to swim.'

She watched her mother skein the wool and steam it in the big steamer on top of the cooker, then dry it, and over a period of a week the garment was completed.

Margaret put her name down at school to go swimming.

The following week, about twenty children set off in crocodile fashion from the school, to the swimming baths; a distance of about half a mile. Each had a towel rolled up under their arms. They had crossed the busy Kew Road, and the equally busy London Road, before filing through the turnstiles of the baths. Margaret felt excited, this was a new venture. Once inside the building they were each allotted a cubicle where they changed into their costumes, leaving all their possessions in the cubicle. Everyone had to wear a rubber hat as well.

As the children walked along the side of the pool, some looked extremely comical in their various homemade outfits. Margaret was rather proud of hers, although she wasn't keen on the colour.

Each child was told to go down the steps into the shallow end of the pool, and was told to hold onto the bar along the side. As the instructor started to demonstrate the rudiments of swimming for the children to copy, Margaret started to realise that all was not well. Her costume was stretching, and as she started to move her legs, it grew and grew, and the weight of the water was pulling it down to her ankles.

Oh Lord, what could she do? She looked round to see if anyone else had noticed, but everyone seemed busy trying out the strokes. She suddenly realised she would not be able to get out of the water, her lovely swimming costume didn't cover her chest any more. Oh, the shame. She tried to gather the woollen fabric around her, but realised she was not succeeding.

The instructor kept urging her to stretch her legs and arms, and she tried to do as she was told, but she was so conscious of the consequences of doing anything that the lesson passed by quickly without her really attempting to swim.

At the end of the lesson, she was the last out of the pool. With as much dignity as she could muster she climbed the steps out of the pool, holding tightly onto the offending costume, and made a hasty retreat into the cubicle, where she had left her clothes.

While walking back to the school, she noticed that two girls behind her were giggling, and she soon was to learn that the object of their attention was herself. They were both in her class, and at break time after school dinner, the two girls were busy telling other classmates about her swimming costume. Her pride was hurt, and she knew she could never wear it again. That evening she told her mother she had decided not go swimming any more, that she hadn't liked it.

'And after I had taken the trouble to knit you a costume,' her mother exclaimed!

Better she didn't know the truth Margaret thought. However, after missing the next swimming lesson, the games mistress waylaid her in the corridor at school and asked her, 'Margaret, I thought you wanted to learn to swim?'

'I did Miss,' Margaret replied, 'but I've changed my mind.'

'Why?' asked Miss Roberts. Margaret didn't know what to say. 'I suggest you come and see me after school,' she said. She was smiling.

'Yes Miss,' Margaret replied, and hurried on to her next lesson.

At 4 o'clock after lessons, Margaret went to the staff room, to find Miss Roberts.

'Ah, there you are my dear, come with me.' She took Margaret along the cloakroom, where she had a locker. She bent inside and brought out a package.

'Here Margaret, I think this should fit you, it is a spare costume I have, I am sure you can make use of it.'

Margaret didn't know what to say. Did Miss Roberts know about her knitted swimming costume? 'Oh, thank you Miss Roberts,' was all she could say, as she accepted the gift and hurried home so she could try it on. It was blue, and made of cotton shirr elastic. Yes, it was perfect, now she could go swimming. How nice Miss Roberts was, Margaret thought, she felt so much better.

Unbeknown to Margaret, Miss Roberts had heard all about the offending swimming costume by overhearing some of the gossip other girls were passing round the classroom. She had felt sorry for Margaret, who was such a pleasant child, and one who really worked hard. Other teachers had commented on how well she was doing.

Just after her eleventh birthday, she took her first music examination. Even her mother was pleased when they learnt she had passed, but that was all. Her certificate was put away in a drawer, Margaret had hoped it would be displayed for all to see. Her mother seemed quite pleased with herself just lately, and seemed more thoughtful and kind to Margaret.

Peggy was growing fast, and had become a real character. Her mother had appeared to be somewhat jealous of her having Peggy, and one day Margaret heard her mother say to Ted that she herself would like a little dog also, only it had to be a pedigree, she didn't want a mongrel like Peggy. How horrid! Peggy was beautiful. Margaret loved her little dog, she was someone to come home to, and Peggy would leap and bound about when she came home, and follow her everywhere.

So Margaret was not too surprised when one afternoon, on returning from school, she found her mother sitting in the kitchen with a little black puppy on her lap. The puppy was licking her mother most profusely, and she didn't seem to be minding. She never let Peggy lick her like that. Peggy was sitting out in the garden.

Her mother turned round as she came in and said, 'Ted has bought me this lovely little dog, don't you think she is lovely? I'm going to call her Susie.' Her mother let her hold the new puppy. Margaret looked down at her. Yes, she was a lovely little thing, with a cold, wet nose.

'I'll take her out into the garden,' she said.

The puppy ran towards Peggy, who suddenly realised there was something going on, and also that Margaret was home. She got up, wagging her tail and went up to the puppy. They sniffed each other, and Peggy followed the little pup down the garden. Unfortunately the puppy headed straight for the pond in the middle of the garden, and before Margaret could do anything, had fallen in. Margaret shouted, and ran towards the pond. At the same time her mother came running out.

Seeing Peggy, she shouted, 'That dog of yours has pushed Susie into the pond, I saw her do it through the kitchen window.

Margaret grabbed the puppy out of the water as best she could, only to have the puppy wrenched from her grasp by her irate mother who dashed indoors and grabbed a towel, which she quickly wrapped around the little dog.

Her mother, who was still in the doorway of the kitchen, turned and shouted, 'That dog of yours will have to go if it harms this one. Just mark my words young lady, you keep it under control or it goes, do you hear?'

Margaret went up the steps of the veranda, closely followed by Peggy, and sat at the top and held her dog tightly. No one would take her dog away . . .

John was never home now. He came in after she had retired to bed most nights during the week. He had told her that he was seeing Elsa three or four nights a week, anytime really that he wasn't working. Margaret had become quite jealous of Elsa. It was because of her that John was never at home. Margaret felt quite lonely, though Peggy helped to fill the void, and she could say anything to the little dog.

*

She was spending extra sessions at the dancing school during October, as everything was continually rehearsed ready for the November production at the Kingston Empire in November.

At the end of October, her mother took her to the dressmakers where she tried on the completed outfits, and was able to take them home. She kept putting them on and admiring herself in front of the mirror, pirouetting and posing.

On the day, they had to arrive at the theatre by 11 o'clock in the morning, even though the matinee performance was not to start until 2.30 pm.

Margaret had been brought from Richmond by Miss Joy, her dancing teacher, as her mother was working all morning. They went in through the stage door, and were put into various dressing rooms. Margaret had been allocated a space in the green room, with about six other girls sharing with her. There were ladies busily curling hair, and applying stage make-up to each of the children. There were lots of clothes hanging up on rails ready to be put on.

Margaret found her outfits, all neatly pressed, and her bag holding her shoes, and in due course, duly submitted to being made up. She sat in a chair, still only wearing her underwear. A towel was placed round her shoulders before two ladies came towards her with sticks of Leichner make-up, some were fat and light brown, and some were slim and coloured, pretty blues, greens and reds.

At the dress rehearsal the week before, they had been shown round everywhere first so that they knew where to go. The stage was vast, and had lots of different curtains hanging. In the wings were all sorts of stage props, and scenery. Just to the side of the curtains were men moving lights about. It had been terribly exciting. Visiting the dressing room had been an experience. The smell of the greasepaint, the costumes, and meeting some of the cast of the production of Rose Marie, which was currently performing each day of the week.

Miss Jay had explained where each child would be at any one moment on the day. To stay in the dressing rooms until called, and then to move quickly to their positions in the wings, ready to go on stage. She assured them that they would be called in good time, and emphasised they must be quiet. Two of the star performers would be changing in the wings, as they had very quick changes, and no one should get in their way.

Once her make-up was completed, Margaret put on her dressing gown and sat and ate the sandwiches which her mother had prepared. The make-up lady had said she would do her lips again when she had finished, but she needed to ensure that everyone's face was basically ready.

Margaret was very nervous, it was a new experience for her. Her mother and her older sister were going to be in the audience, and Ted had said he would try to be there to watch her. Except for a school play, and singing in the choir, she had never performed in front of an audience before.

There was a lot of chatter, and her dancing teacher was rushing around checking everything, and answering a lot of questions. Margaret looked at herself in the mirror. She looked so different with the heavy make-up on. Her eyelids had been painted bright blue to match her eyes, and her lips, having been re-touched up, were bright red. She had lots of rouge on her cheeks, and she was perspiring profusely as she was so warm.

Time passed quickly, and it was soon time to put on her first outfit, in preparation for her first routine. Even though she thought so herself, she really looked good in the silk and tartan outfit. She was to play the part of the boy. Her partner was putting on the frilly dress in which she looked so good. It was very flouncy, and stood out around her, made of lots of white tulle and ribbons. In her hair she wore tartan ribbons which contrasted nicely with her long blonde hair, which had lovely ringlets spilling down. She really looked a picture.

Ten minutes before the curtain was to go up, they made their way up to their positions in the wings. The orchestra played a fanfare, the music began. The big arc lights circled the stage, and came to rest on Mrs Joy. She gave a short introductory speech, and once more the music resounded around the auditorium.

Mrs Joy nodded to them as their introduction music played. They moved out onto the stage, and into the bright lights. The middle curtain went up.

Margaret sang for all she was worth:
  *"A you're adorable, B you're so beautiful, C you're a . .
."*

. . . they moved around the stage, moving to the music, and on completing the tap routine, posed while the audience clapped most profusely. It was over. Phew!

Margaret and her partner moved off the stage and returned downstairs to the dressing room, where Margaret changed into her ballet dress, ready for the Jewels ballet. It took her some time to get the flowers into her hair, and to set the little tiara she had been given, on the top of her head. It was difficult to make it stay upright, but eventually with the aid of one of the make-up ladies, and lots of hair clips, it stayed in position.

She had a little time free before she would be called for the ballet. She checked everything was all right, that the ribbons to her ballet shoes were done up correctly and secure, and that her tutu was in place. The make-up lady dusted her face with powder, and gave her a drink of water.

She looked around watching everyone else preparing for their parts. The prima ballerina was wearing a beautiful dress in oyster cream, and the girl playing the part of the onyx jewel looked absolutely fabulous in her black tutu and sparkling jewels. The chorus were all in emerald green and sapphire blue.

She returned to the wings, and waited for the next cue, when she would once more move onto the stage. Her teacher had choreographed the ballet beautifully. All the dancers were representing different jewels. She herself, being the ruby, had a major solo part to play, but the star was the pearl, who would step out of a big oyster on the stage.

Margaret made her way to the entrance spot, and at the precise moment ran out to the centre between the chorus, and raised herself onto her points. She began her routine which ended with her positioned next to the oyster, which gradually started to open, revealing the pearl.

There was much applause when the ballet came to an end. They had three curtain calls, and lots of flowers were handed up onto the stage for the solo artists. Margaret received a lovely spray of chrysanthemums and carnations.

At last it was all over, and she returned to the dressing room to change into her ordinary clothes. She carried her bag containing her outfits, and her shoes, as she made her way out of the stage door.

As she left the theatre, her mother, Ted and May were all there. She felt so proud. They all congratulated her on doing so well. Perhaps she was someone after all. Perhaps they did like her. She felt like a Queen.

* * *

Chapter 15

Christmas came and went. Her mother provided lots of food, but there was very little money for gifts. Margaret made Ted some pipe-lighters out of newspaper, and made a little pot to put them in by painting a jam jar, and then adding little painted flowers. Ted would always light his pipe by lighting some paper which he put into the fire. Now he could have nice folded ones. She made little lavender bags for her mother to put in her lingerie drawers. There was lots of lavender in the garden, and she had found little scraps of pretty material to make the bags.

Having saved up her pocket money for three weeks, she had bought John a bar of Fry's Chocolate Cream.

The goodies she received included a woollen scarf from Ted, a school satchel from her mother, and a plastic umbrella from John. Her older brothers and sister never sent anything, and didn't come to the house for Christmas either.

When May had come to the Kingston Empire she had been very pregnant, and just after Christmas her second son, Clive, was born. Margaret was longing to see this new baby, but her mother told her that May would not be coming until January, and only then if the weather was reasonable.

*

So 1947 dawned. It was bitterly cold in January and February, and there was lots of snow. Her mother told her that Ted had bought another house in Kew, which would be better than having to pay rent, as they did for their present house, and that all being well they would be moving very soon.

Margaret was quite certain in her mind that Ted had bought their present house in Mortlake. She loved their present house, and couldn't understand why they had to move again so soon. Her mother had said they would be moving to a brand new house, it had just been built and would be more modern. It could never be as nice as this one, and there would be no veranda.

When Margaret went to see it she was most disappointed. The garden was very tiny, and there was lots of builders' rubble strewn all over the place. The house was situated in a small avenue. The rooms downstairs were larger, and it did possess a separate toilet and bathroom upstairs, but otherwise she would have preferred to remain in the house in Kingsway.

She told Peggy all about it when she returned home, and the little dog licked her mistress and nuzzled up to her as if to assure her it didn't matter, they would still be together. Margaret was feeling very low and sad, and the only thing that gave her any comfort was her little dog, whom she adored.

She was busy doing some homework that evening when her mother came in from work and told her she had received some sad news earlier that day.

'You remember Angus dear, don't you,' she began. Margaret nodded, and her mother had her undivided attention. 'Aunt Clara has written to say that her beloved Angus died a few days ago of tuberculosis. She must be so distraught, Angus was such a lovely young man.'

Margaret stared at her mother dumbfounded. Angus dead! It couldn't be. She knew he had written to say he had been ill, and true she hadn't received any further letter from him during the summer months, but he just couldn't have died.

Tears ran unchecked down her face, she ran from the room and upstairs to her bedroom and threw herself on the bed, her whole body was wracked with sobbing. It was some time before she was able to compose herself, but her mind kept floating back to her visit to Scotland the previous year, and her memories of Angus. His kind, gentle ways, and all the things he had taught her while she had been in Scotland.

How could he have become so ill? He had written to say he was getting better, and hoped to go home from the sanatorium. No amount of reasoning seemed to help her come to terms with the loss of her hero. Her mother let her read the letter from Aunt Clara. It was true. How she mourned his passing, and it was many days before she felt any better, and many months before she came to terms with the loss.

*

Over the next few weeks everything was once more packed away in boxes ready for the move.

Margaret soon learnt she had a long walk to school from the new house, which meant getting up really early, so that she could take Peggy for her walk before she left.

In April she took a further music examination, Grade 2, which she passed with ease. She had taken ballet and tap exams also, which had been quite frightening at the time, but all was well, she had passed all of those as well. The one person who showed pleasure at her triumphs had been Ted. Little did she know it was his money that was financing her.

On learning that she had passed her exams, he gave her mother some money so that she could buy Margaret a new best dress. She hadn't had a new dress since she had first come home from North Wales. The dress chosen was lovely. A silky blue fabric, with a white collar. She looked very smart in it. Her mother said she could wear it to Church the following Sunday. Since moving to Kew she had become a regular churchgoer once again, and attended St

Andrews Church on the common, near the entrance to the Royal Horticultural Gardens at Kew.

Her only sadness was that she couldn't take Peggy with her, but she enjoyed going, even if it was on her own.

Since moving she had also become friends with two girls, Janet and Josie. Both of them came some distance to attend the service. They had, ironically, both lived in this area, and their respective parents had each moved to Ham, the other side of Richmond. They told Margaret that they would both soon start attending a church near to where they now lived on Ham Common. It was even more ironic that within a very short while, just months ahead, that Margaret learnt that she would also be moving to Ham, and Lock Road.

Both Janet and Josie became good friends at school, Margaret had a lot in common with Janet, who also played the piano and was taking her exams about the same time as herself. Janet was the sensible one of the trio, and was liked very much by the teaching staff. Another girl, called Carol, joined their group. Margaret liked her, but soon realised she was trouble, just like Betty had been in Wrexham.

The months ticked by. She became used to the new house, but disliked it intensely. She hated the long walk to school each day, and the time it took to get to and from her dancing school. But she was continually busy, and never went to the Royal Hotel any more. She always had unhappy memories of Patch, and the little dark, back room behind the bar.

As the summer months stretched out before her she realised that her life was one long round of learning, but at least she was becoming old enough to care for herself.

She saw little of her mother, they appeared to pass like ships in the night. So it was some surprise when Mrs Trent told her that they would once again be moving, to Ham, the other side of Richmond, and that she could go with herself and Ted when they went to the house they had purchased, the following day.

It was a long bus ride, but the bus stopped right outside the house they were to live in. It was an end of terrace house, with a large garden. Her mother told her that the small bedroom would be hers. It was very tiny, but it had a window seat with a good view of the road, and also across the grass expanse where three roads joined. Alongside the house was a pathway which led down to Teddington Lock on the River Thames.

Margaret was thrilled. Her two best friends lived just a short distance from the new house; now she would have some friends of her own living nearby. Both Janet and Josie went to her school. Much to her surprise, her mother took an instant liking to Janet, as well as Josie, when she brought them home for the first time, a week after they had moved in. Her mother had taken the trouble to offer them something to eat and drink.

So this time she was pleased to have moved. Ted told her the reason for moving had been that the house at Kew had been Leasehold, whatever that meant, where this one they now owned was Freehold. He didn't envisage they would move again.

There had been one fateful day some two weeks before the move that Margaret would sooner forget. She had come home from school to find Peggy had been missing all day. *Oh no, not Peggy,* she thought. She looked everywhere. Her mother said she had not seen the dog since before lunch; Margaret had roamed the area for hours, but eventually had to concede she was unable to find her. Peggy would never have gone off on her own, she was sure of it. But an extensive search over the following few days revealed nothing. She went to the Police Station, but they had not been advised of any stray dog.

Up in her bedroom, where she seemed to spend so much of her time when she had lived at Kew, she constantly thought of the cuddly little dog, with her sad brown eyes, and her understanding ways. Peggy had always understood when she was unhappy, and they had so much fun together when Margaret felt happy. Little Peggy would jump around and get excited. Now she was missing. Was it just coincidence that both her little dogs had disappeared? Her mother's dog Susie was a nice little dog, but she belonged to her mother, and kept a respectful distance from Peggy. Now she was missing Susie still stayed near to her mother.

Margaret shared her unhappiness with John one evening. He seemed to be listening, but offered no comment. This confused her. John always took her side, and made such good suggestions, but he seemed distant, as if he knew something, but wouldn't tell her. On another of his rare appearances he told her that he would soon be called up into the Army. Margaret blamed Elsa for occupying all his spare time. How unfair, she thought, John was her brother.

May came to visit and brought Terry and the new baby. Her mother was all over the new baby. All Margaret knew was that the baby seemed to take a lot of time and attention, and cried a lot. It was as well they paid a visit before the family moved, as there was more room in the house at Kew. Although the house they were to move to was much nicer, it would be very cramped as they had so much furniture.

Two days before the move Margaret heard her mother telling May that Peggy was not with them anymore.

'Where is the dog then mother?' she asked.

'Margaret didn't know that Peggy was having puppies, she had got out a couple of weeks before. All the dogs around kept coming up to the door, I had to have her put down, I was not prepared to have a lot of puppies everywhere making a mess.'

Margaret couldn't believe her ears. Her mother had had Peggy put to sleep, how cruel. She would never forgive her mother for this. Margaret took herself off to the local church and found some solace inside the beautiful building. She sat quietly on one of the pews, and cried. No one seemed to care. When she finally returned home, her eyes red and swollen, no one asked why she was upset. She wouldn't give her mother the satisfaction of knowing that she knew what had happened to Peggy, but she would never forget.

May only stayed two days, and then took the boys home to London. Margaret had overheard her telling her mother that she was unhappy, her husband often became drunk when he was home on leave from the Navy, and often hit her. *Goodness, thought Margaret, why did her sister tolerate staying with him?* On the other hand, where else would she go? There would be no room at the house they were moving to, especially now she had two children.

On the day of the move, Janet had come round to the new house and helped her friend, carrying things into the house from the lorry, and putting them away as instructed. It was obvious that her mother liked Janet the best. Margaret thought this might be because Janet played the piano so well, as well as the idea that she might be a good influence on her daughter.

The following day the three chums set off early in the morning for school, taking the bus. It was about four miles to the school, but at least they would be going by bus each day, almost door to door, and there was no walking to do like Margaret had done in Wrexham, or when living at Kew.

Life once more settled down into a comfortable pattern. It was a long, hot summer, which allowed the girls to meet often, go on picnics, and watch the local cricket match each week on Ham Common. They were all good at sports, and were soon members of the school netball and hockey teams.

Margaret's life was full, what with her dancing lessons, music lessons, the many examinations set her, her sporting events, and school homework. The weeks flew by.

At the end of term concert there was a prize giving, and Margaret was very proud to be called onto the platform to receive a prize book for her excellent work on scripture. It was a beautiful bound volume of *Jane Eyre,* a book she loved, written by Charlotte Brontë.

In July she learnt that her brother John had to report to the Army. He told her that every male over 18 years of age had to be conscripted for two years. Her mother had told her that he was to go to Catterick Camp in North Yorkshire, and would be away for some weeks doing his basic training. She thought she would miss him a lot, but she didn't. She supposed it was because when at home he was either working or at Elsa's.

On his first leave he did spend some time at home. She later learned that her mother had insisted that he did. He had looked so smart in his uniform as he came up the garden path. She was so proud of him. Her mother soon set tasks for him to do, such as digging the garden, which was fairly vast, and repairing all sorts of things in the house.

Margaret was currently practising a very hard piece of music called *The Rustle of Spring* by Sinding, ready for her next piano examination, which was to be held at the Royal College of Music in London. She had recently been up to London with her music teacher to the College, which was situated just behind the Royal Albert Hall. It was a very impressive building, with many rooms leading off long corridors. The room they occupied had an enormous Steinway grand piano. The music sounded so much better played on such a majestic piano, but she found it hard work to actually operate the foot pedals, she felt she needed longer legs.

She told John she was struggling with this particular piece of music. He promised her two shillings if she could play it well before he had to return to his regiment, The Royal Signals. It was just the incentive she needed. She spent hours at the piano over the next few days, and within a week she had mastered it well. The two shillings was hers. She also earned extra funds from him by cleaning his uniform, ready for his return to barracks. It was hard work cleaning all the buttons, and blanching belts and gaiters, but she liked doing it for him. He, on the other hand, made use of the free time by going to see Elsa. And then he was off again.

She passed her music exam with flying colours, thanks to John. Her world consisted of competing. She had a zest for winning, to show everyone that she had talent. She would have liked to have been able to tackle Sociology, but she had no help in this direction, except books she borrowed from the library, but no one helped her to understand them, At the back of her mind there was always the notion that she wanted to be a Children's Welfare Officer, like Mr Green in Wrexham. She loved her music and dancing, but her heart wanted something else.

Her mother, who had listened to her yearnings from time to time, quickly told her that when she was just a little older she would probably have children of her own, and then she would probably wish she hadn't hankered for them, especially when they kept her up at night, or made a mess, or didn't do as they were told. Her mother just didn't understand.

Ted gave up working at the hotel and took a job locally as a general labourer. Her mother also left the hotel and started working at the local public house as a barmaid, which was really what she had been doing at the hotel. Still, she didn't have to travel far to work any more.

Now that Margaret was old enough, she was allowed more freedom, and enjoyed meeting her friends. She had recently taken to walking Susie along the towpath down by Teddington Lock. Margaret was fascinated with the boats, and the way they rose and fell with the water level as the boats went through the lock. Sometimes the little group of friends would walk right along the river path as far as Richmond. It was so beautiful along this stretch of the river.

She played the piano so well now that her music teacher at school encouraged her to play the piano at the end of term concerts, but her own mother never came, she always said she was too busy. This term she played Schubert's *Serenade.*

The girls often went to the cinema. Janet was besotted with Robert Donat, and Margaret idolised Anthony Steele. He was her hero. They both sent off for film star photographs of their idols, and carried them around with them in their satchels. All of the girls loved animals, so it wasn't too hard to understand their love of two recent films. They saw *Lassie Come Home,* which was originally screened by MGM in 1943, but was recently shown at the local cinema. Then came *National Velvet* starring Elizabeth Taylor and Mickey Rooney. Both films had been so sad the girls had all come out crying. The most recent film had been *The Yearling* staring Gregory Peck. They all agreed that he was so handsome. But nothing would change Margaret's mind about Anthony Steele.

That same year, Margaret passed an Art Exam at school, and won a scholarship to Kingston Art College. Her mother agreed that she could attend on Saturday morning part-time, but she could not take up the scholarship on any full-time basis. The college agreed to this, and Margaret spent her 3d pocket money on large sheets of paper and charcoal, and soon learnt how to improve her skills in drawing and sketching.

Although every day of the week was busy, Margaret realised that she was far from happy. Having her friends around helped, but inside she was lonely.

Over the last six years she was aware that her life had been in total trauma. The war had a lot to answer for, it seemed to have broken up her family, segregated her from so much. Most of all there was the great divide between her mother and herself.

When they had lived in Upminster, her mother appeared to love her dearly, but since returning from evacuation there seemed to be nothing left of that love. Margaret was just a burden. She had believed that her mother had given her material things on her return, only to discover that Ted had been paying for everything. She wasn't his child, but he appeared to care for her the most. Or did he do it to please her mother? Who was to know? She only knew how unloved she felt, and wished and planned for the day when she herself could show them all that she would win. She would be good at everything she tried, she would go to college one day, and she would achieve her dream.

It was up to her to prove her mother wrong, and in her heart of hearts she knew she would not tire until she had reached her goal. She felt so emotionally battered from years of loving and losing, she could empathise with anyone.

She knew what it was like to be parted from her mother and family, and the heartache of being fostered by three entirely different families. The Jones family who had used her, Mrs Perie and Pamela who had loved her and given her so much, and Mrs Hall, who had meant well, and had actually taught her to be independent in some things. They had all been so different. Different standards of living, and different outlooks on life.

She recalled the longing she had to return home, and her great disappointment that things had changed, and realised that she felt an outcast and so lonely.

She had lost so much, Mrs Perie, Pamela, Mr Green, friends she had made along the way, Judy and Pat, her little dogs Patch and Peggy, and of course dear Angus . . . and John, he was still living but entirely removed from her world. No, life would never be the same again. The little girl from Upminster had grown up and become the mixed up, independent, determined person she was today.

There was no way she would ever be able to love her mother again. How she had disliked Ted, but he, on the other hand, appeared to care about her, and perhaps they were now better friends. Who knew what the future had in store for her? But of one thing she was certain, she would meet any challenge head on, and win. No one would ever take that away from her . . . ever . . .

* * *

About the Author

Jean Reddy was born in London in 1936, and lived through the blitz as a small child before being evacuated in 1942.

Her early life provides the background she vividly creates in this novel.

This is her first novel, and begins to reflect her very controversial life, which continues in her following two books.

She now lives happily in North Hampshire with her husband, Harry, and surrounded by her large family, who all live within a fifteen mile radius.